Matthew Godfrey

THE INSANITY OF IDEAS

www.theinsanityofideas.com

ISBN Paperback 978-981-18-0292-8

Cover design by cherriefox.com

First edition. 2021

For Dorothea, Orion, Austin, and Alyxandra.

INTRODUCTION

Humanity's extensive back catalogue of innovative ideas is unparalleled, incredible and often awe inspiring. The wheel, electricity, sanitation, medicine, energy, art, agriculture, architecture, computing, space travel, music and even the chocolate eclair. All are objectively brilliant and unmatched on the planet. We collectively accomplished all this with the relative speed and ease of a super-intelligence compared to all the other species that crawled, slithered and swam before us. Bold, beautiful and breakthrough ideas that have saved lives, sparked happiness and propelled us magnificently and supremely forward. Unfortunately, our resume is also blotted by a body of tremendously egregious ideas as well. War, slavery, inequality, racism, pollution, terrorism, crime and extinctions would all be high on that list of shame.

Where do we stand now? With our powerful tools, knowledge and intellect, are we in the prime position to select only the best ideas going forward? Or will the growing cacophony and pace of available ideas, circulating in our minds, cities and screens, outstrip our ability to correctly assess their merit? Alternatively, should we now actively delegate this critical responsibility to the very ideas that we are now creating? Is that complete insanity, to be avoided at all costs, or an evolving, inevitable, insatiable reality? Either way, we are all going to find out very soon.

CONTENTS

CHAPTER 1

WHAT IS AN IDEA?

Antoine Laurent Lavoisier was a gifted visionary who materialised truly ground-breaking ideas for his time. He was both an aristocrat and a wealthy scientist, born in 1743 into the turmoil of 18th century revolutionary France. A few of the incredible ideas he was involved with include the creation of the metric system, the first list of all known elements, the naming of oxygen and hydrogen, and predicting the existence of silicon. He was also very passionate about creating innovative solutions to improve Paris' hygiene, water, and air quality. His mind continuously bubbled and fizzed with ideas. The lucrative Tobacco industry was also attractive to his sharp intellect. He devised and set the standard for the precise amount of water required to enhance a pleasant smoky flavour without destroying the stability of the tobacco. Apparently, 6.3% is the magic number, but it was an idea he would later live to regret. One of his most insightful ideas has since caused seismic scientific ripples. He is credited with discovering that all matter is neither created nor destroyed.[1] In his view, once matter had exploded into existence, the universe, in its wisdom, deemed that it was thereafter, eternal.

Unfortunately, revolutionary France didn't quite agree that Lavoisier was a bonafide genius to be treasured by the people. On Thursday, May 8th in 1794, his very inquisitive mind was permanently separated from his wealthy body by the sharply indifferent blade of a guillotine. On that day, his Father-in-law also suffered the same fate, as well as twenty-six other souls accused of crimes against the people of France. Amongst their charges were tax evasion, as well as fiddling with the water content of Tobacco to line their own pockets with deceitful profits. For these crimes, his brilliant head was permanently divorced from his body, placed in a common-sack and buried in an unmarked grave.

If he had any last thoughts, it may have been to consider himself a very lucky man to only suffer this fate. The idea of the guillotine had been first employed for execution in France just two years earlier, starting in 1792.[2] Prior to this date, public executions frequently favoured a popular medieval device called the "breaking wheel". The idea was a simple one. Strap a freshly convicted prisoner to a large wooden "X" and then, using an iron bar, brutally smash all of their bones and joints at strategically placed notches. These notches created small depressions directly below the limbs to allow a cleaner and crisper snap in the bones when struck. Usually, the clinical iron blows started at the feet and worked painfully but precisely up the limbs, which had been tightly strapped to the cross. When the guilty had been clinically bludgeoned into a corrugated broken mess, the criminal's bloody body was then entwined amongst the spokes of a wheel, where crows would then be invited to generously peck at the still-living flesh. An excruciating death may still be days away unless the executioner kindly decided to employ the optional idea of a "coup de grâce" which translates to "mercy blow" in French.[3] The customary favour was usually the iron bar generously smashed across the heart.

A year after Lavoisier's relatively swifter and more pleasant death, the French State quietly admitted that they may have had the wrong opinion of him and sent a belated note of acquittal to his widowed wife.[4] By this time, it was of little consolation to either Mrs Lavoisier or the decayed and buried corpse of her husband. Shortly before his beheading, he wrote a lamenting letter to his cousin in which he said, "I have had a fairly long life, above all a very happy one, and I think that I shall be remembered with some regrets and perhaps leave some reputation behind me. What more could I ask?"[5]

His request for a legacy of reputation was eventually fulfilled. He is now widely regarded as the "Father of Modern Chemistry"[6] and his name now lords over the city of Paris, as the civil engineer Mr Gusatvee Eiffel, bestowed Lavoisier with the posthumous honour of permanently engraving his name on the North-West face of his iconic Eiffel Tower.[7] His ideas on the eternity of matter, now called "the conservation of mass," has since evolved to have a lasting impact on modern science and how we view our world. Einstein's even more famous idea on the powerful tango between energy and matter, enshrined in $E=MC^2$, and Fred Hoyles' concept of a "Big Bang" which proposes the mechanism that unleashed all matter in the Universe, are both ideas that arguably share their roots with Lavoisier's unique insights. Moreover, centuries of subsequent experiments have proven his bold ideas on the nature of matter as being fundamentally correct, even if the Universe may eventually entropy its way to a frigid, dispassionate pool of particles trillions of years from now.

Today, science is convinced that mere nanoseconds after the Big Bang, all the seemingly infinite material in our Universe irrevocably erupted into being. Why this happened may always remain a mystery, but Lavoisier's relative eternity of "the conservation of mass" is now difficult to be denied. For aeons, the trillions and trillions of particles created at the seminal moment have since been constantly rearranged, manipulated, fused, and even split by the most powerful forces that nature has assembled. Fourteen billion years later, virtually all of this matter is still defiantly and stubbornly standing in one form or another. Amazingly, every single particle required to composite everything humans are and all planets and life-forms, already existed, and was passively loitering around a galaxy waiting for either an energy or perhaps an entity to give it movement or purpose. From the atoms that combined to form the synapses in Lavoisier's brain, to the calcium in the bones of your body, or even the ethanol molecules in your next tequila shot. All of the core building blocks of every atom has been innocently, silently, and patiently awaiting their assembly instructions for billions of years. The lego pieces of the probable, improbable, and almost impossible were created in an instant after the Big Bang and have been waiting for cosmic instructions ever since.

The Universe is designed like an eternal Ikea catalogue and humanity is just the latest intelligence continually fumbling with the instruction guide, box by infinite box. We act like a small conspiracy of freshly educated lemurs, tucked into a microscopic corner of a vast jungle, trying to assemble wondrous artefacts armed with little more than a wrench, flange screws, and randomly assembled genes. We are only limited and guided by the laws of physics which have been slowly revealing themselves to Lavoisier and others, as immutable.

The ideas humanity creates, on the other hand, appear to be the very opposite to the firmly resolute natural world. Ideas are more intangible and ephemeral. They require energy to create but seemingly have no true mass as they are not strictly restricted in scope by the amount of space in our brains. Big thoughts can be tucked into small places. There are no limits on imagining them, the scale of them, or the vast quantity of ideas we can create. Yet, like the physical matter they are born from, they definitely exist, as we all effortlessly conjure millions of new ones into existence every day.

An idea in its simplest form is an internal thought, which if realised, promotes a change, choice, or action in our physical reality. The world created by humanity has no shortage of them. Almost by definition, ideas are forward-thinking as they attempt to configure the future in a desired direction or outcome. Therefore, ideas are essential to human progression, as they point in the same direction as time and evolution. Without ideas, there can be no small advancement or giant leap forward for our species, in fact, no civilisation of any kind. No buildings, no bombs, no bitcoins, no buttered toast. Only the raw impulses and instincts that inhabit our ancient "reptilian" brains would exist. These may be superbly well suited to guide and define a repetitive daily existence to eat, reproduce, and survive. However, they would never create satellites, surgery, the Sistine Chapel, or Seinfeld sitcoms.

Whether our ideas have been inadvertently manufactured from our dreary daily commute or gifted from a divine and inspirational source, only a rare few of them make the metamorphosis from our imagination into reality. Most of our ideas will evaporate out of the cosmos as quickly as they were conceived. From the collective universe of all of humanity's ideas, only a select few succeed to see the light of our sun. Fewer still are deemed worthy or successful enough to live on the planet across generations. If our ideas stand the test of time, they are often the exception rather than the rule. We only need to look back a decade in the photo album of our species to find ourselves continually staring at our chosen ideas and collectively saying "What where we were thinking?" Ideas previously judged as awesome now seem awful, and those that our ancestors once abhorred might now be sublimely addictive.

Our species can't solely be blamed for selection errors in the ebb and flow of transient ideas. We are spoiled for choice. Estimates vary, but on average we each manifest up to 60,000 thoughts per day[8], and a large proportion of these thoughts could be classified as ideas. Others may be filed away as fears, anxiety, reminiscing, or just memories. These are emerging thoughts that evoke the structures of our past but leave us like eunuchs in altering it. Only forward-thinking ideas have the true potential to affect our growth, prosperity, momentum, and ultimately, our fate.

Every day there are billions of new ideas floating in humanity's global synaptic ether that we all need to select from to forge the future. Most of these ideas would be rightly regarded as small, pithy, or inconsequential ones. Others might be revolutionary or inspiring. Perhaps others are deeply horrifying, hurtful, or unspeakable ideas. The bulk will disappear almost as quickly as they are formed in our minds. Forgotten and evaporated with no trace left behind. Others will be selectively communicated to incite action in either ourselves, our friends, our colleagues, or perhaps, the country. When ideas are brought to our attention, we are all required to judge which are to be embraced and chased or which should be ignored.

As both individuals and a species, we constantly and increasingly need to answer a daily question; is an idea good or bad? How do we decide if the ideas we create and those that are presented to us are ingenious or insane? Does such an objective distinction even exist? Or are all ideas eternally subjective and the merits lie only in the minds of the beholder? If ideas are the seeds for the future development of our lives, society, civilisation, and therefore species, can we be entrusted with selecting the best ones and rejecting those that can harm us? If so, which people are best equipped to make such decisions? Governments, corporates, markets or individuals? If not them, then who will take responsibility for selecting the ideas that empower our future and should we build tools to help us make these decisions?

Like those created by Antoine Laurent Lavoisier, will our ideas stand the test of time, and will future generations proudly etch our names on their own magnificent monuments? Or will our ideas fail, create confusion, or drive division? Will we get lost in our choices and stunt the growth of our society like a broken, riddled strand of DNA on an evolutionary tree? Or more dramatic still, will our ideas grow a life of their own? Will they ultimately learn to generate their own ideas, increasingly take control, select, and then action the ideas that will govern the future of humanity? Will our ideas no longer be slaves to our will and evolve completely out of our control with opinions of their own?

Welcome to the insanity of ideas.

CHAPTER 2

EVOLUTIONARY IDEAS.

The Bird's Head Seascape is arguably one of our planet's most important marine areas for bio-diversity. It is a pristine marine park that covers over 2,500 islands and coral reefs, speckled between the coasts of West Papua and Indonesia. It is home to at least 70 unique species of reef fishes, corals, and crustaceans that are found nowhere else on Earth. It remains pure as, luckily, the majority of people have never heard of it or had the chance to visit it. Given how most tourists behave, perhaps it's best that we keep it this way. The incredible diversity and specialisation of species is the reason why leading marine biologists regard it as a "cauldron of evolution"[9] and a living research centre to understand how Darwin's theory of evolution plays out in a truly virginal eco-system.

The ground-breaking concept of "Natural Selection" is now an idea that is often taken for granted by modern biologists, having first been published by Darwin in 1859 in his landmark book, "On the Origins of Species."[10] It is now firmly cemented as scientific gospel in the majority of educational institutions around the world.

However, for Darwin himself, the creation of his seminal idea was a long and arduous one to germinate. His journey towards his theory on evolution began twenty-eight years prior to the original publication date when he set sail on the HMS Beagle in 1831. Darwin at the time was a fresh graduate from the University of Cambridge and only twenty-two years young. The voyage he embarked on would last almost five sweaty, salty, weather-beaten years, as the Beagle slowly bobbed its way around the coasts of South America and Australia, before returning to England in 1836. The hundreds of new and exotic species and environments that Darwin would observe had a profound influence on the idea that was brewing in the back of his brain.

History records that Darwin was not even the first choice to be the naturalist on HMS Beagle. The original selection was the Reverend Lenard Jenyns. At one stage, he apparently accepted the idea, started packing and then later declined, citing ill-health and vital duties to his local parish. Ironically, despite his medical complaints, he eventually outlived Darwin by over a decade. The golden ticket to sail into the unknown was hurriedly passed down to the unsuspecting Darwin. He was given only four weeks notice before the Beagle planned to leave Devonport. He initially declined the offer, following the advice of his father who felt the idea would be a waste of his son's time, but he eventually recanted his views and subsequently funded his son's trip.[11] Darwin accepted the invitation, and his revolutionary ideas and his deserved legacy subsequently sailed into science books.

Despite the enormity of the subject matter, his idea of evolution was elegantly simple. He summarised it as "any being, if it vary however slightly, in any manner profitable to itself, under the complex and sometimes varying conditions of life, will have a better chance of surviving, and thus be naturally selected."[12] In other words, genes randomly mutate and create subtle, yet new, possibilities. Some are good and propel the species forward, and some are bad and limit or curtail its future. Gene mutations could be considered as the "ideas" of the biological world. It has often been that these biological "ideas" have underpinned the evolutionary advantage of everything on Earth from dinosaurs to dentists. Darwin's idea challenged many entrenched existing religious notions that the origin of all species was by the hand of God. Unsurprisingly, the Catholic Church did not officially comment on Darwin's idea, and held its pious tongue for almost one-hundred years until 1950, when Pope Pius XII described it as "valid".[13]

In modern society, all around the world, Darwin's idea would now undoubtedly be classed as a firm scientific theory, supported by ample evidence. For many people, it is now a stone-cold fact of nature. However, even when this idea has now had 150 years of rigorous research and debate there is frustratingly, and perhaps surprisingly, no unanimous human agreement as to whether it is indeed true.

Recent research indicates that up to 18% of American adults, or almost fifty-million people, currently disagree that Darwin's idea of natural selection is a good idea. This data also correlates with people's political persuasions, as a 2007 Gallup poll indicated that 68% of registered Republicans do not believe in evolution.[14] They apparently dispute any "so-called" evolutionary facts and are firmly on the eternal side that man is made in God's image and plan.[15] As ingeniously insightful as he was, if Darwin believed that getting people to rapidly accept his ideas was going to be simple, he was wrong then and would be still wrong today. The topic of evolution is a debate that has bubbled on for over a century between communities, scientists, educators, and religions. Despite all archaeology, research, and discussions, humanity still can't seem to unanimously settle the discussion on whether it truly is a good or bad idea.

Evolutionary "ideas" defined by gene mutations are often brutally and objectively adjudicated by the mechanism of "survival of the fittest" and are binary in nature. Either a species thrives and lives, or it fails and dies and buries its genes with it. For billions of years, genes were the only form of ideas on the planet. The relatively new emergence of ideas created by humans exists in stark contrast to evolutionary ideas, as they are often more subjective. Cold facts, data, and evidence can be brushed aside by the heat of opinion, faith or bias. Bad human ideas can sometimes survive, even thrive, and not be automatically destined for extinction by the environment like their genetic idea equivalents.

Luckily for our planet, Dr Mark Erdmann of Conservation International[16] doesn't subscribe to the majority of the Republican's objections to Darwinism and is a member of "Team Evolution". He has dedicated a large proportion of his career to underwater research at the picturesque Bird's Head Seascape. He studies the creatures that live there to peel back the pages of evolution and shine a light on how the insightful prose of Darwin's ideas crawls and swims in this tranquil sea.

One such beast that captures his scientific attention is a rare species of shark. For over 450 millions years, sharks have been happily prowling the oceans. Well, not always happily. They have narrowly avoided global extinction at least three times[17], so give respect where it is due for this ultimate survivor. They enjoyed roughly 150 million years on the planet before the Dinosaurs emerged to graze the Earth, and they are still in their prime long after the last Tyrannosaurus-Rex came a little too close to a plummeting meteor for its liking. In all these aeons, there have been millions of shark generations and countless variations, but the basic chassis and floor plan has remained virtually unchanged. They are a triumph of evolution, as no matter the changes in their DNA that offered a variation in their species, the core components of a shark were deemed superb by natural selection and were retained for the survival of the fittest.

To add intrigue to this journey, Dr Mark Erdmann is researching a newly discovered shark evolution at the Bird's Head Seascape that may one day, millions of years from now, provide an evolutionary advantage. The intriguing Epaulette shark can walk. Incredibly, there is a species of shark that has adapted to allow it to walk either between coral heads, at low tide, or across the ocean floor. Pause and ponder how simultaneously fascinating and terrifying that is for the future. It's concerning enough to many that sharks are lurking just beyond the breakers waiting to mistakenly eat prime cuts of Captain Quint. However, sharks evolving to a point where they could potentially stroll out of the surf in a few million years? That would be a sight that only Steven Spielberg would truly appreciate.

"Instead of swimming around, these little coral-dwelling sharks actually "walk" using their pectoral and pelvic fins, which makes it easier for them to poke their heads under coral and rocks as they look for small fish, snails, and crustaceans to eat," explained Dr Erdmann.[18] "Amazingly, we discovered that walking sharks evolved just 9 million years ago, making them amongst the "youngest" sharks on our planet."

Although this evolutionary innovation is very worthy of Dr Erdmann's intense focus, arguably these sharks have been dragging their tiny fins a little. They have had at least nine million years to take advantage of the evolutionary idea they have been gifted. In comparison, humanity has done much more with the gifts that we inherited. Our distant ancestors first learned to walk upright around 8 million years ago[19] and our species has accomplished a great deal with this genetic idea. The epaulette shark, on the other hand, has enjoyed an extra one million years as an advantage over all walking hominids on life's game clock and, to be brutally honest, they have yet to craft as much as a vivid haiku let alone launch a new iPhone.

The comparative benefits of this adaptation for this shark are therefore perhaps either marginal, or the benefits are specific to the environment it finds itself in. Dr Erdmann is best placed to opine on this conundrum. What is clear is that the Epaulette shark has no intellectual capacity to have any concept of its existence and cannot objectively distinguish between when it is walking or swimming, or any other state for that matter. They are ruled by their genetics and their environment. What powers the engine room of a shark's mind is the fuel of impulse and instinct. Hunt, eat, mate, flee, smell, explore, and even socialise.[20] All important, life saving "thoughts" but all could be considered as impulse or instinct and not "ideas". As far as we know, no shark has had a single idea pass through their Y-shaped brains[21] in all 450 million years they have been patrolling the oceans. Otherwise, they may have invented all manner of things by now.

Sharks and almost all creatures on Earth are merely carriers of genetic ideas elegantly sprinkled within them by evolution. Random changes in their genetic code are spun like icons in a Vegas slot machine and deposited in their bodies without control or consent. Then the environment, predators, sex, and death are the ultimate adjudicators of whether these genetic ideas are ultimately good, bad, or will trigger life's jackpot. If it results in a better life, the idea is deemed beneficial for evolution and is naturally selected as Darwin surmised. If it accelerates a shorter life, the idea is classed by evolution to be "bad" and more often than not, discarded from the planet. The actual owner of the genetic code is only a passive spectator to this timeless and often ruthless evaluation. The genetic idea is not theirs, nor is it one of their making, and they have no say in the matter even with the most skin in the game.

Evolution is a cold assassin. It judges biology's random genetic ideas on a binary, dispassionate, and objective basis. Life or death. For over 3.5 billion years[22] all ideas on Earth were evaluated without an ounce of subjectivity, and the only concepts on the planet were genetic ones. The fossil record is history's back-catalogue of good and bad genetic ideas that were progressively and naturally sorted by evolution. This has worked exceptionally well and remained unchallenged for almost a biological eternity.

The first embers of a revolution only sparked relatively recently with the emergence of what science calls "object permanence", or the ability of a species to understand that objects continue to exist even when they are no longer detected by their senses. Although object permanence has been on the planet for millions of years, Swiss psychologist, Jean Piaget, was among the first to study this in children during the 1920s[23]. Object permanence is likely an essential foundation stone that needs to be laid prior to the emergence of an idea that is not genetic. To have the capacity to understand that an object, if taken away, still exists and may return in the future, requires a species to have a rudimentary understanding of the arrow of time. Ideas are an internal thought which, when realised, promote a change, choice, or action in reality, and time is the tapestry that all ideas are woven upon. Ideas are conceived to create, change, or influence something that has not yet happened, but will occur if that certain course is taken. Ideas are our minds ability to peer into a possible future and then seek to build it.

It may be naturally assumed that evolution first pioneered "object permanence" in our species. It emanates in our mammalian frontal cortex and it is evident that we have the run of the planet. If the origins of humanity can be traced back for six million years[24] we could potentially assume that object permanence dates back to a similar age. That may be so, but when such a metaphysical evolutionary trait first emerged can be hard to pinpoint exactly. However, certain species such as crows, whales, and octopuses all seem to have their own degree of object permanence[25] and their evolution predates human existence by millions of years. The fossil record for whales dates back 50 million years[26] and DNA evidence of crows can be found 30 million years ago.[27] The resilient and remarkable octopus eclipses them all and is truly the old man of the sea. Their lineage dates back by well over 200 million years, and have been extensively documented as having a very high level of intelligence extracted from their unique combination of up to nine separate brains.[28]

Octopuses also seem to have a special ability to adapt to their environment. Captive octopuses have been observed to recognise and behave differently toward the various individuals that study them. In one science lab, a captive octopus, for no obvious reason, took a disliking to a particular scientist. Whenever that scientist passed on the walkway behind the tank, the octopus decided to spurt a stream of water down the back of her neck.[29] Stefan Linquist, of the University of Guelph in Ontario, has studied octopus behaviour and concluded that octopuses are aware of their surroundings: "When you work with fish, they have no idea they are in a tank, somewhere unnatural. With octopuses, it is totally different. They know that they are inside this special place, and you are outside it. All their behaviours are affected by their awareness of captivity." Even more surprisingly, there is documented evidence that they know how to use tools to improve their chances in life. They collect, clean, and carry shells to use as shelter and one species even carries poisonous tentacles from the Portuguese man o'war. It ingeniously wields them to deliberately sting both passing predators and prey alike.[30]

This is all anecdotal evidence that octopuses have rudimentary forms of ideas. Some are useful, some are cheeky, but all can be interpreted through the lens of an idea. They appear to be internal thoughts that will have an impact on the reality they observe, recognise, and remember. There are many of these accounts, as well as scientific evidence that octopuses can solve very challenging puzzles and exhibit memory, learning, and cognition capabilities.[31]

This body of evidence suggests that octopuses do not only have object permanence but may also have ideas. As they are a species that predates humans and even whales by hundreds of millions of years, this releases the tantalising potential that object permanence first emerged in the ocean and perhaps the very first genuine ideas on the planet did so as well. In the late Jurassic period, while the land was barren of ideas yet packed full of plants, insects, and supercilious dinosaurs, beneath the gentle waves there perhaps was a species of octopus, quietly bubbling and brimming with a myriad of the first and only ideas on the planet. It is impossible to know their mindsets, and perhaps science will never be able to confirm whether prehistoric octopus "ideas" ever existed as tangible evidence will be, by nature, very elusive. Ideas are transitory and unless their impact can be found in the fossil record, it is pure speculation that an octopus was the first-ever species to have ideas of its own.

For now, mankind holds a firm, opposable thumb grip on the very first idea on the planet. Science has unearthed indisputable proof in the form of the 3.3 million-year-old stone cutting tool. It was discovered, almost by accident, by archaeologists Sonia Harmand and Jason Lewis of Stony Brook University.[32] Researching the Kenyan Rift Valley, situated in northern Kenya near the Ethiopian border, their focus was on the dusty shores of Lake Turkana, the world's largest permanent desert lake. It is an oasis housing over sixty species of fish including tiger, cat, pufferfish, tilapia, and Nile perch, as well as the odd angry crocodile. One morning in July 2011, the scientist accidentally took a wrong turn and arrived in a previously unexplored area. Instead of turning back and squandering the day, the archaeologists fortuitously decided to survey it. What they found pushed back evidence of the first idea on Earth by at least 700,000 years. They named the site "Lomekwi 3" and recovered dozens of ancient stone cutting tools, including flakes, cores, and anvils. Their findings would be subsequently listed as one of the top archaeological discoveries of the decade by the Smithsonian.[33]

This evidence signposts a game-changer in human development as it indicates that prehistoric humans were translating their ideas of tools into physical reality earlier than previously understood. There are multiple competitive advantages in using stone tools including chipping bark, crushing food, cutting meat, stripping hide, and even breaking into bone marrow. What is truly innovative here is that these stones were shaped by hand and not naturally formed. At least 3.3 million years ago, one of our ancient ancestors had the idea to grab a rock and deliberately chip, flake, and refine it into a tool that had previously only existed in their imagination. What's more, is that this was potentially a learned skill that was shared amongst members of the tribe. It, therefore, hints that other embryonic ideas were also being formed at the time to facilitate the development of cutting tools, such as early forms of communication.

The genesis of the stone tool idea may have been to replicate a naturally sharp bone, or the realisation that the accidental splitting of rock has new benefits, or perhaps it was simply a God-given bolt of inspiration from the divine. Either way, this is the first proof we have that an idea exists on Earth. Emerging from a vacuum of four-billion years where the random sequencing of genetic ideas had ruled the planet and defined the success or failure of a species. These new and original ideas, from the minds of hominids, quietly presented the middle finger to the power of evolution. Good ideas, expressed as physical tools, made the holder more likely to survive than their genetics alone. If two apes had identical genes, then the one that created and wielded the stone tools would have a competitive advantage. This advancing ape, armed with the first idea of a stone tool, was now slightly less dependent on natural selection alone to be the fittest to survive. They had the potential to eat more or be better protected from environmental elements. Ideas immediately became a technological edge in survival which none of the billions of creatures that had previously existed on planet earth, had ever truly wielded before. From this defining moment 3.3 million years ago at Lake Turkana, humanity's domination of the planet, using the power of their ideas in defiance to the pure genetic ideas of other creatures, had truly begun. Other creatures may have been naturally endowed with genes that ensured they were stronger, faster, or fitter, but from that moment on, our genes had given us conscious ideas that would enable us to conquer all species that came before us. Viva la revolution.

Arguably, ideas and not just biology alone, have since changed the trajectory of life on the planet. Slowly at first, but at a relentlessly accelerating rate. Now at a pace faster than could ever be mustered by the relatively slow and random tinkering of evolution alone. For example, almost every advantage humans have in modern life has been either partly made or shaped, in some sense, by the core idea of a cutting tool conceived aeons ago. Whether it's the clothes that you wear, the pages of a book, the screen on your phone, the chair you sit on, the food that you eat, the car you drive, or the home you live in, they all involve a cutting device of some form to create or assemble. Following the original elegantly crude stone tools, mankind has since invented countless sophisticated and refined variations of the same basic idea. From the magnificently precise Honjō Masamune samurai blades to the delicate slices of a Bard-Parker surgeon's scalpel, there is no empire, no industry, no Louis Vuitton handbag, without the ideas of a prehistoric ape preceding it. All the subsequent cutting devices humans have engineered can be considered as derivative ideas.

They trace their provenance back to this original idea that was manifested on that African shoreline all those millenniums ago. True, there have been continual refinements, dramatic additions, and new materials incorporated but the core root of the idea is both immutable and undeniable. When you slice your serrated steel knife into a medium-rare filet mignon at Wolfgang Pucks' new steakhouse, you are standing on the shoulders of what seems to be the first good idea ever materialised by man or woman in history. Intriguingly, it's probably not even a human idea.

Indeed, our ancestors may have stolen it, like an upstart comedian secretly hearing another's best bit and desperately dropping it into their latest set. Humans were not yet evolved 3.3 million years ago when these stone tools were first being made. Our species, Homo sapiens, is only around 300,000 years old.[34] We belong to the genus Homo[35] and the earliest discovered fossil from our direct line of ancestors, Homo Habilis, currently dates back 2.5 million years ago.[36] Therefore, these stone tools predate our known direct lineage by roughly 800,000 years. Either our understanding of Hominids is still incomplete, or it appears that the first animal in history to conceive or act upon an idea was a competing bipedal ape called Australopithecus or another hominid, Kenyanthropus.[37] If this data is correct, our direct ancestors may have "inherited" this breakthrough idea of a cutting tool from earlier generations. Perhaps our species has plagiarised the very first idea ever to exist from these near-forgotten apes. It could also be true that this innovation may have been created separately and independently in multiple locations, but the more evidence scientists find, the more the signals point towards a transfer of technology. We just may have to credit the underlying success of our species from this stolen spark of an idea. Humans; stealing ideas since 3-million BC.

The anonymous ape that conjured the world's first idea for a cutting tool also needed another skill in their bag of tricks. The ability to self-evaluate their idea and predict whether it was good, based on whether it solved the problem they were trying to address in the first place. They needed a way to process ideas or what could be described as an inbuilt "mental algorithm." This may have been as simple as calculating "more meat = good, less meat = bad" but that innovative ape needed to not only have the idea of a cutting tool but also a mental framework to evaluate whether to embrace, refine, or discard the idea. The mental algorithm to judge an idea needed to be born for ideas themselves to flourish. Time, trial and error may have been a large proportion of development, but the ape needed the unique capacity to subjectively evaluate the merit of their ideas against the original intent. Up until this point in history, evolution had been both dispassionate and objective, as random gene mutations were the only "ideas" on the planet and survival itself was the operating algorithm of selection. The incredible ability to rudimentarily, but subjectively, assess an idea and determine if it offers a competitive advantage, prised open the door to a new way for the fittest species to survive and exponentially leverage their given and gifted genetics.

Having the ability to mentally evaluate ideas and filter the good from the bad, is arguably just as important to survival as having the idea itself. After all, an ape that continually has bad ideas and executes them isn't likely to be surviving long and won't pass its advantages forward in time. This ancient ape's fledgeling mental algorithm needed to be operational enough to sieve the rough stone diamonds from the worthless dustbowl of ideas.

The mental processing speed of these apes evaluating ideas might have been frustratingly slow from our perspective. Like patiently watching a child assemble a 1,000 piece jigsaw puzzle, you might feel compelled to dive in and help. Their brain capacity, at around 450 cubic centimetres, was similar to a chimpanzee, yet considerably less than modern humans at 1,350cc.[38] However, our ancestors did make steady, sustained progress with their ideas, and by 2-million BC, the next evolution of their cutting-stone idea, the hand-axe, can be found in Kenya.[39] These are significantly more refined, crafted, portable, and effective than the beta-version stone tools that their ape predecessors used 1.3 million years before them. At the time, these new tools would have been the engineering equivalent of trading-up in power and speed from a Model T to a Tesla. These cutting tools were likely chiselled by Homo erectus, who was one of the first apes of our Homo genus and thus, an ancient relative to us all. It could be argued that these stone tools simply leveraged the previously established concept devised by the original ape innovators. So these ideas, while significant, could also be viewed as derivative and not truly original.

The earliest evidence we have for an original idea adjacent to our Homo genus doesn't arrive on the scene until around 1-million BC. The very first idea that our species can legitimately claim a patent to was how to control and contain a fire. The Wonderwerk Cave site in South Africa is an archaeological site that has been studied since the 1940s. It wasn't until 2012, however, that Dr Francesco Berna, an archaeologist from Boston University, found the burning evidence for this breakthrough.[40] Patiently waiting a million years for him to walk into the cave were the ash remnants of burnt leaves, grass, and even bones. A scientific review of these sediments using advanced techniques such as a micro-morphological analysis was undertaken to understand their provenance. The ancient ash had jagged edges, showing that it was not burned elsewhere and blown or washed into the cave, which would have worn such edges away leaving a smoother topography. This data indicates that the fire was created inside the cave and was deliberately "man-made". Given the area and time period, the most likely hominid to claim copyright to the complex idea of creating and controlling fire, is indeed, Homo erectus.

This amazing and inventive hominid sits proudly in our ancestral tree. Perhaps the control of fire is humanity's first original good idea that we haven't borrowed from another competing ape. How Homo erectus made the fire is less clear. Flint sparks, a branch transferred from a forest fire, or friction are all possible. Further clues may be still buried in the cave, but the many competitive survival benefits of the idea are abundantly clear. Warmth, light, safety, and better nutrition to power a hungry brain. The control of fire was a new tool driven by an underlying need to advance our natural selection and it marks mankind's insatiable and often irresponsible entry into the energy industry. A sector we have been lucratively exploiting ever since.

Although Homo erectus operated with roughly 60% of the brain capacity of modern humans[41], they were incredibly inventive with the biological hardware that they had. They were also the first species of hominid who had both the ability and motivation to travel. Evidence of their existence has been unearthed in Africa, Spain, China, and Indonesia.[42] Their ability to either form or build upon the ideas of previous apes, and then determine which were good for survival, may be a key factor behind their proliferation. There is even some evidence to suggest that they had formed their own primitive language, which may have been an essential component for sharing ideas within a tribe or passing them on from generation to generation.[43] Despite their innovation, their relatively brief, yet flourishing time on Earth, eventually evaporated. The last archaeological evidence of their activity is dated to be approximately 117,000 years ago.[44] That means for a period of a few hundred thousand years they would have lived parallel to, and may have competed with, Homo sapiens for resources.

Research from the Australian National University leans towards "laziness" as an underlying cause of extinction for Homo erectus.[45] Archaeological evidence suggests that they made little effort in acquiring resources for tools, improving them, or extracting the most from their environment. Compared to their neighbours, Neanderthals and Homo sapiens, they didn't respond well to environmental challenges, and when things changed they didn't have the skills to adapt their ideas for the new circumstances and died out. As innovative as they were, they might be the original "couch potatoes" of the human family tree. Slack-jawed in their caves, happy with their favourite stone axes, without the energy and curiosity to push themselves further.

Despite these early ground-breaking ideas by competing apes and our ancestors, it took modern humans a great deal of time before we would genuinely recognise and appreciate their brilliance. When Homo erectus held a rock, it saw the potential for a tool, and through ingenious skill and sweat transformed them into an axe for a competitive advantage and the enhancement of its life. The modern and more intelligent humans that would follow them thousands of years later didn't always share the sharpness of both their insights and ideas.

Up until the 1700s, medieval European farmers would sometimes discover these discarded ancient axes in their freshly turned soil. They would often be mistakenly anointed with the mythical status of "Thuderstones."[46] Believed to have fallen from the sky during a wild storm, created by the God of Thunder. They were not recognised as the fingerprints of our ancestors, unearthed in a burial mound by a decisively deep plough. Instead, the ideas that Farmers and society created for these magical Thunderstones were often much more diverse and imaginative. They could either protect the owner from lightning strikes, be used as a powerful medicine, ward-off trickster spirits, or even help divine for gold. They were a prized find, a gift from the gods and not the chiselling of an ancient ancestor.

In 1723, the leading botanist Antoine Laurent de Jussieu politely pointed out to the influential French Academy, that these objects bared a striking similarity to other stone weapons already being procured from around the world and may well be stone axes.[47] Despite this idea now seeming both benign and obvious, it took over a hundred years before it acquired mainstream acceptance and overturned the entrenched superstitions of the Thunderstones. This was primarily due to the fact that, up until then, Christianity had been resolutely faithful to another idea that Adam and Eve were the first humans on the planet and did not actively engage in creating ancient stone weapon systems while dining on the apples of Eden.

It was medieval society's mental algorithms, defined by culture and dogma, that prevented their experts from recognising the true innovations from the hominids of the past. Modern humans are exponentially more intelligent than Homo erectus, but our ancestors may have laughed at the medieval scholars as being quite dull for their repeated failure to comprehend the mundane but exquisite usefulness of their hand-crafted "Thunderstones".

This demonstrates that the origination of an idea is just one part of extracting the maximum value from the idea to propel the human species forward and provide an evolutionary advantage. Our mental algorithms used to judge an idea and classify it as "good", may similarly be critical to our society's future success.

Our mental filters constantly change over time as they're impacted by culture, context, knowledge, and experiences. By the time the 1700s had arrived, humans had passively constructed a more convoluted and subconscious series of algorithms to judge the multitude of ideas that they were bombarded with daily, compared to the rudimentary framework developed and deployed by Homo erectus. Religion, medicine, superstition, prosperity, and advancements in forging cutting tools had coded an entirely new mental operating system which was then used by humans to evaluate all ideas. This new code was so distinct from the original mental framework, that when medieval humans held and evaluated evidence of the earliest and 'most' original hand-crafted ideas ever to arrive on the planet, it was wildly interpreted as evidence of the supernatural and divine. The idea, encased in a stone tool, remained unchanged from the day it was made, but humans subsequently analysed, perceived, and interpreted the idea to be completely different in both form and function.

Rather than judging ideas by how they help an average ape survive the day, as Homo erectus may have done, humanity had evolved other criteria to assess the plethora of new ideas that we encountered. This is not restricted to our clumsy interpretation of ancient stone tools. As our society has progressed, our mental algorithms have also become more complex. The ones we now use to evaluate ideas focus less on daily survival, and increasingly more on other priorities. Ironically, some of the parameters that our mental algorithms now incorporate for idea selection, may no longer completely align with the core requirement of survival of the fittest.

The renowned archaeologist, Dr Richard Leakey, dedicated much of his life to the origin of our species and, as a result, has discovered many of the oldest tools ever created. During his career he also observed the evolution of how people process ideas. In 2008 he lamented that "we are now most certainly the only animal that makes conscious choices that are bad for our survival as a species."[48] An interpretation of this biting criticism is that the mental algorithms of the earliest humans deployed to evaluate ideas were beautifully simple and pragmatic. The volume of ideas that our earliest ancestors were juggling were both few and infrequent. The only success criteria was for an idea to deliver immediate improvement for daily survival. For millions of years, the pace of innovation for our ideas was relatively slow and, therefore, the pressure to select new ideas was similarly sparse from a generational point of view. However, over time, the relentless progression of both the sheer quantum of ideas and the complexity of our mental algorithms has expanded and become more opaque. As our society, culture, populations, and ideas have morphed and scaled, this has impacted our ability to select ideas with clarity. It has become increasingly clouded and no longer judged by the pure elegance of "survival of the fittest."

As Dr Leakey articulated, we are now the only species on the planet that wields the mental algorithms to select ideas that may lead to our detriment rather than our success. All other species delegate their survival primarily to the ideas contained in their genes alone. Only humans have hacked their biological systems to introduce ideas that can supersede the evolutionary power of genetics. Worryingly, this can lead to us engaging with destructive ideas that may ultimately result in the elimination of individuals, tribes, civilisations, or even an entire species.

Homo sapiens first walked the Earth around 300,000 years ago.[49] Since then, we have collectively created and executed millions of amazing, beautiful, and inspiring ideas. However, we have simultaneously selected and enacted many bad ones as well. Our mental algorithms, designed to help us select ideas, are not infallible. Ideas that may have seemed like perfectly good options at the time of consideration, may only seem like they are in our best interest. With more time, experience, or knowledge, it may eventuate that we have selected ideas based on a selfishly short time period and often discount consequences that extend beyond our immediate reach, horizons, or lifespans.

Armed with the power of ideas, our species survived and prospered to eventually spread from the plains of Africa to dominate the planet. For the last ten thousand years, our civilisation has unleashed a relentless army of idea expansion. Stone-age technology, impressive as it was, had limitations of both reach and impact when compared to the capabilities of the ideas devised in the iron, industrial, nuclear, and information ages. Throughout most of our history, the ability for humans to share new ideas and the global volume of all ideas was relatively limited. Therefore, the consequences of executing our ideas were primarily localised in nature, or relatively slow to spread across communities, countries, and continents. Ideas, good and bad ones, could also be more easily lost across generations given the limitations of accurately storing and sharing data in a stone, and even iron-age, world. In the last one hundred years, all of this has dramatically changed. In this time, the global population ballooned from around 1.6 billion in 1920 to now 7.8 billion people.[50] The scale and potential impact of both good and bad ideas have also exponentially increased in terms of speed and quantity to a point where there is now a virtual tsunami of ideas washing across the Earth daily. This is especially true when compared to the thin trickle of ideas our ancient ancestors faced.

As a species, are we well-equipped to judge this torrent of new ideas? Has the growth of our mental algorithms, to assess ideas, kept pace with the volume and speed of ideas that we now need to judge? To ensure the survival of the fittest, individuals and an entire community must be compelled to act upon ideas that are best for continuing prosperity and discard those that endanger it. Will our inbuilt mental algorithms, now inexorably coded by our culture and society, increasingly drive us to choose ideas that will negatively impact our species' success and limit our true potential as foreshadowed by Dr Leakey? Or can we rise above the melee and continue to orchestrate and dominate the planet with a sustainable and balanced purpose?

CHAPTER 3

THE IDEA EXPLOSION.

O ver the last 300,000 years, the combination of our slowly escalating and evolving ideas, together with our inherited biology, have recorded many more triumphs than either could have achieved alone. Over precisely the same length of time, our genetics have not significantly evolved an inch, and just as importantly, our brain-case has remained relatively consistent over this entire period.[51] The biological hardware that has propelled humanity for a millennium has not had a significant update for at least the last few aeons. The dramatic improvements allowing humanity to dominating the planet may have been due to our cognitive, cultural, and collaborative upgrades, rather than our genetics or biology that gave us the opportunity in the first place.

All other species on Earth rely predominately on their given genetic-code to drive their impulses and instincts for survival. Humanity has hacked this ancient, primordial system and then progressively built upon our undoubtedly gifted genetic code to add self-generated ideas that are designed to enhance our competitive status. This empowered humans to survive and excel. Our ideas enable humanity to no longer be at the mercy of our environment or a competitor's strength and speed. Ideas give humanity an evolutionary edge to extract more out of any given situation than our brilliant biology could achieve alone. Although success from this evolutionary edge may now seem like it is fait-accompli, extinction for the human race came much closer than most cappuccino sipping customers in a Starbucks, would know. The unique power of ideas was almost wiped from the Earth by the immense fury of nature.

To study, measure, and compare the relative destructive power of volcanos, science created the "Volcano Explosivity Index" or VEI. The scale starts at zero and goes up to a mighty level eight. The only reason it's limited to eight is that science is yet to discover any evidence of a volcanic explosion that dials it even higher.[52] The affluent Romans, vigorously discussing the vices and virtues of Emperor Titus while drinking red wine in the bars of Pompeii, were amongst the very first to witness a punishing VEI 5. Mount Vesuvius erupted on August 24th 79 BC, subsequently greeting the citizens of Pompeii with 1km³ of molten ejecta, killing approximately 10% of the population or at least 2,000 people. This blast was so devastating that it buried Pompeii in ash and preserved it as a warning note from nature. It now attracts up to 4 million tourists per year to marvel at this motionless cataclysm.[53] However, the almost unfathomable energy released during a level 8 explosion reduces the Vesuvius eruption to a delicate lava soufflé, as they can be up to 10,000 times more powerful. Science has identified forensic evidence of up to forty-seven different VEI 8 eruptions that have left deep scars in the geology of the Earth.[54] Only one of these natural subterranean monsters has blasted during the reign of Homo sapiens.

74,000 years ago, a chart-topping VEI 8 eruption occurred at Toba, Sumatra in Indonesia. It was the largest explosion on Earth for over two million years.[55] This super-volcanic eruption violently thrust 1,000km³ of burning ejecta into the atmosphere, blanketing a large proportion of the Earth in ash. This is an equivalent volume of ejecta as 19 million Empire State Buildings simultaneously exploding into molten rock and powder in the Earth's atmosphere.[56] The effect on the climate was terrifyingly profound. Some accounts suggest a "nuclear winter" ensued for at least six years, crippling the food chain and the environment across the planet.[57] Animals and plants were challenged by the unexpectedly aggressive climate and either adapted or died. As a result, the global population of Homo sapiens may have plummeted to as few as 5,000 hungry and dusty people, hunkered down in southern Africa.[58] Many scholars cite this event and this band of survivors as "ground-zero" for our precariously shallow gene pool. This drives the concept of the "Mitochondrial Eve", where the X chromosomes in everyone alive today can be traced back to one common female ancestor, who tenaciously and stubbornly survived this holocaust.[59] This relatively small population of humans likely prospered because the environment they were in was simply much less affected by the blast.[60] Or, was it was their unique, spontaneous ideas that enabled them to become the fittest to survive and pass on their genes to the future? There may have been some members of the tribe who's metal algorithms were wired slightly differently to conceive better ideas that helped deal with the onslaught of this crisis. The framework to judge their ideas, under what must have been intense pressure, may have helped them escape this ravenous near-extinction event.

During the first two million years on the planet, our ancestors wielded ideas like stone tools that offered a glimpse as to what our species would eventually be capable of. After the bottleneck of the Toba explosion, our species has increasingly armed itself with a relative cathedral of creativity which has resulted in humans dominating the planet and becoming the first species in history capable of ending all other life on Earth. Although the massive destructive power of our nuclear ideas only releases the energy of a BB-gun compared to a VEI 8 explosion, we have devised many other ideas that could either directly or indirectly drive both ourselves and other species, extinct. In the evolutionary arms race, the natural power of genetic code led the first 4 billion leisurely laps around our sun. It steadily and incredibly created countless creatures with genes mutations that would either result in fabulous prosperity or fossilised purgatory. With the arrival of Homo sapiens, the random ideas of genetics met a revolutionary competitor for directing the future of a species. The volume and scale of humanity's ideas have been relentlessly gathering pace and momentum. Feeding upon themselves like a snowflake slowly surging into a slab avalanche. Ideas have become a nitrous-oxide supercharger that has propelled the biological chassis of mankind to slowly overtake genetics as being central to the determination of survival of the fittest. The ideas that have increasingly flowed from humanity in the many centuries following the Toba explosion have been as dramatic and as impactful as any volcanic eruption. Toba is an inflexion point, as after we survived that near-extinction event, our species launched from the hot ashes and truly took flight.

Before the dramatic events at Toba, science has unearthed archaeological evidence of at least three transformative ideas imagined by our species that many other innovations in our civilisation are derived from. These being the creation of tools trade and the harnessing of energy. In the millennia following the Toba explosion, science has uncovered evidence for many new and essential ideas for human domination of the planet. These include language, painting, agriculture, architecture, astronomy, medicine, spirituality, and even war. In truth, some of these ideas may have crystallised in our ancestors' minds earlier, but the evidence is either inconclusive or more archaeological research needs to be completed. Perhaps all traces were simply wiped from the Earth in the Toba explosion, or even subsequent cataclysms, that periodically and dispassionately swat species from the earth forever.

The human idea of art and painting is inspiring, sublime, timeless, and emotive. It is also an essential way to communicate and importantly record complex ideas between close social groups over generations. It may also be another one of humanity's stolen ideas. The earliest documented cave paintings date back to at least 65,000 BC. They purposely and majestically reside in a cave in Iberia and were likely crafted by our often defamed cousins, the Neanderthals, as the site predates the arrival of Homo sapiens in Europe.[61] In rust-red minerals on a limestone canvas, the image silently drifts the artist's ideas forward through the ages like an ancient emoji in a time machine. Animals and geographic shapes are just some of the images that the Neanderthals were compelled to record. The exact purpose is unclear as experts can only study the context and interpret the images accordingly. Perhaps science's interpretations are insightfully accurate, or perhaps they are as insane as our recent ancestors, looking at chiselled rocks and seeing Thunderstones. We may never know their true meaning or the intent of these long lost artists.

Pablo Picasso is widely credited with the admission that "good artists borrow, great artists steal." If Neanderthals were truly the originators of all art on this planet, there is no shame in Homo sapiens admitting that we then elegantly appropriated their idea, even if we did subsequently stand by and watch them go extinct.[62] They did not disappear without a tracy, after all, many people on the planet still have a small percentage of Neanderthal DNA entwined in their bones.[63] Some of our species' most wondrous and incredible moments have flowed from both the ideation and execution of pure art. If it was a gift taken from the Neanderthals, it was a beautiful one indeed.

The archaeological record does, however, give humanity sole claim to many other monumental and Earth-changing ideas. One that has been especially favoured by the majority of Kings, Queens, and Politicians is the powerful idea of war. Of all of our ideas, surely this is has been the most horrific and destructive, and one that has no true equivalent in nature. Unfortunately, we have also become exceedingly good at perfecting it. Defensive wars against an invading brutal ideology may be inescapable and perhaps even essential. However, in all of human history, how many offensive wars have been objectively justified? The analysis may always be a matter of subjective opinions to adjudicate upon. Upon analysis, we may ultimately find that most wars have been more related to other distinctly human characteristics, such as greed, ego, power, wealth, and resources, no matter what noble spin they have been given by the triumphant scribes of history.

Many species in the animal kingdom have internal conflicts and physical combat that often results in individual deaths. This killing can be exceedingly prolific in terms of a female insect eating its mate after coupling, or a mature lion ending the lives of its rival's offspring to increase the prospects of his own. However, humans took this almost universal basic animal instinct and extrapolated it with a horrific new idea. The mass-murder of our adult species to gain material or psychological resources. As Harvard biological anthropologist Richard Wrangham once said, "when it comes to killing adults, humans really are exceptional."[64]

Our first proven descent into cold-blood killing is currently pinned to the location of Nataruk, in modern-day Kenya. What is now scrubland was once the shores of a tranquil lake in 10,000 BC, where a tribe of at least 27 fellow men, women, teenagers, and children were spending their day being butchered in the sun. We know this to be the case, as their bodies fell directly upon their shadows, instantly cut down by brutal blunt force trauma. Left for dead in the shallows of the lake that gently draped the corpses in a shroud of sedimental for archaeologists to later uncover in 2016.[65] The murder weapons of choice were wooden clubs and spears tipped with sharpened obsidian rock. One of the victim's hands may even have been bound before their skull was crushed, suggesting that there was a degree of purpose, patience, and premeditation to the murder. This event is the first recorded evidence of a mass killing in the history of humanity.

Our vicious journey towards this violent idea had taken aeons. The first evidence we have for sharpened axe tools is circa 2 Million BC, and the first proof of using these tools in an act of barbarous war is a very distant 10,000 BC. Curiously, humans engaging in the trading of resources can be dated much earlier to potential flint exchanges in 150,000 BC. To barter for resources was an idea that had already been well established centuries before.[66] The archaeological records are either far from complete or imply that "war" is a relatively fresh idea for humanity. It appears that we had the idea for tools, energy, art, language and trade for millennia before we had gathered around a campfire to collectively brainstorm the idea of "war" on a whiteboard.

The optimist may view this relatively late development to start slaughtering our kind as an indication that we are intrinsically peaceful as a species. For hundreds of thousands of years, we apparently made more love and less war. An alternative perspective is that the emergence of this idea shows that our species' mental algorithm to judge which ideas are good or bad has either taking a sharp decline or at least a turn towards a more selfish or destructive direction. We held in our hands the stone weapons capable of mass-murder for over ten thousand centuries, yet there is no discovered fossil evidence for mass-murderous atrocities earlier than Nataruk. Could it be that the less-civilised humans were more peaceful, we are yet to find evidence, or that they just hadn't conceived the idea earlier? Our present society struggles to pass as much as a decade without unleashing a new destructive idea on our fellow nations. It is plausible that this now repetitive behaviour can be blamed on strands of DNA alone? It seems to be a quintessentially human idea to mass execute our species, and we should not abdicate all of the ideas that we find abhorrent to our uncontrollable inherited biology.

After our species had a taste of this historic massacre in Nataruk, then perhaps future wars and weaponry were always going to be an inevitable path that humanity would follow. In the same vein, given enough time a car may be the natural outcome of the idea for a wheel, world war might be the eventual outcome of the murders of Nataruk. This event may be the first domino that created a chain-reaction of ideas through time, that finally clicks over at the successful creation of a nuclear bomb. Once we conceived destructive wars to gain a material advantage, we could no longer delete it as a choice from our mental algorithms. In the short term, this may have been a strategy that promoted the survival of the perpetrators of the massacre, but over time, favoured the most aggressive members of our species. The short term gains from war were not always weighed against the potential long term consequences to our species. As our ideas of self-destructive weapons exponentially increased, it is far less certain if they are for our society's benefit and may result in a much darker future. It is this type of relentless idea evolution that compelled Albert Einstein to say "I know not with what weapons World

War III will be fought, but World War IV will be fought with sticks and stones."[67] To paraphrase, our ideas will ultimately lead to our destruction and devolution as a species.

As sunrise dawned in 5,000 BC, we were still genetically identical to our ancestors born 300,000 years earlier, but our myriad of ideas had multiplied and been deeply embedded into new societies. They helped to organise our environments so we could be infinitely fitter and fiercer, to survive and thrive like no other animal before us. Our species' trajectory was just beginning to be delicately decoupled from the long, exclusive relationship with our unique genetics and growing increasingly tethered to the ideas we had created. Of equal importance, was our skill in executing only our best ideas and hopefully discarding our most destructive ones. What humans really required to accelerate domination of all other living things, was no longer just progress in the achingly slow and tauntingly random genetic mutations in our DNA code. We needed fresh ideas, bigger and better ideas, to give ourselves a competitive edge. Then we had one. It would grow to become both monumental and planet-changing. We called it "The City". Once we had flicked on this light bulb of a concept, our species took a giant leap forward and has never looked back.

The author and innovator, Steve Johnson, insightfully identified the collaborative power of what he termed "Liquid Networks."[68] His concept suggests that new ideas are less likely to spontaneously emerge in any form of social isolation. Ideas require a fluid system of information exchange, where facts, observations, and existing ideas are blended, morphed, and multiplied inside a social network to generate new directions to emerging problems. A city is one such liquid network, as it increases both the data points and volume of human social exchange. As it grows, the opportunities for collaboration increases, which multiplies the potential for new ideas to spawn. Ideas themselves are like ingenious Lego pieces. They click together to form something new, built on foundations that have both innate and random connections to each other. It, therefore, stands to reason that the more Lego blocks that a tribe has access to, the more new concepts can be built to gain an advantage for that group. We may all subjectively feel that ideas are miraculous beams of light, emerging spontaneously from the ether. In reality, they are a mental merger of existing notions that click together in our minds to create an idea that only appears to be entirely new and distinct. Like when a child builds a house made of Lego, to them it may look new, but it's highly dependent on the individual blocks being within reach, to begin with.

Humanity's idea for "The City" is built upon the important Lego brick of an earlier idea, "agriculture" which can be traced back to around 10,000 BC in what is now Turkey.[69] Farming was an alternative idea to the previously dominate nomadic, hunter-gatherer lifestyle humanity pursued. It created food surplus, shelter, stability, security, and division of labour. It enabled specialisation in crafts, tools, and increased the potential for trade and barter. Importantly, compared to living in smaller disconnected tribes, a larger population of minds concentrated in one place would dramatically increase the interactions, connections, collaborations, and the opportunity for ideas to potentially click together. By 4,500 BC, cities were emerging in Mesopotamia, and the city of Uruk (located south of Baghdad, in modern-day Iraq) is arguably one of the earliest and most important cities in history.[70] At that vibrant moment in time, over 10,000 people enjoyed living inside the freshly bricked clay walls that had been erected to embrace the boundaries of their newly invented city.

The inhabitants of Uruk were busily rubbing their minds together to ignite new ideas for the benefit of their society, and eventually, other neighbouring cities that were developing. As a result, entirely new concepts of worship, governance, security, laws, specialisation in skills, trade, social classes, and architecture were frothing at the surface in cities like Uruk. All these new and important ideas for humanity laid their foundations in the rich soil of the emerging cities in Mesopotamia. Although they have since been incredibly enhanced, evolved, and often radically twisted, the core ideas that have underpinned much of our present civilisation were ignited here. One of the reasons we regard the ancient ideas of Uruk as being amongst the first is that they are uniquely well documented. The citizens of this city were also among the first to immortalise their daily ideas and activities in thousands of written clay tablets. Many of these have survived to tell their story. Preserved forever by being buried in the dry desert sands in the silent ruins of their once magnificent city.

They were also some of the first people to expand on the emerging idea of materialism, which has since become a central part of modern civilisation. Cylinder seals have been found at Uruk, which were designed to stamp ownership over a document or a property.[71] This implies that the concepts of reputation, honesty, trust, and theft must have been a part of the growing fabric of the early cities, as the cylindrical seal was a valuable stamp of personal identity. For thousands of years, cylinder seals were highly personalised, worn on a string like a necklace and prized by all levels of society. Both the rich and poor utilised them to claim authority over physical items that belonged to them. To lose one, would be today's equivalent of exposing oneself to "identity theft", and would cause the owner as much concern as a New Yorker leaving their wallet on the subway. Modern society has now evolved this original idea, developed at places like Uruk, into many different forms of identity and ownership including the concept of a "patent" where an idea itself can now be legally reserved and attributed to an individual for material gain. This underpins much of modern entrepreneurialism, innovation, and capitalism.

For millennia, generations of traders, families, priests, kings, and slaves in Uruk grew their city to be a regional centre for power, influence, and fresh ideas. It peaked as the largest city in the world in 3,000 BC. For the first time in history, 80,000 people were boxed into a dense space, bouncing ideas off each other like a colossal, experimental pinball machine with the city's evolving wealth, expansion, influence, and prosperity tallying the score.

Around 2300 BC, one of the first documented ideas of the flesh is also recorded in Uruk. The Priests of the city operated a temple-brothel which was dedicated to their goddess, Ishtar, and it was home to women of three distinct ranks.[72] The highest grade of women were designated to perform sexual acts in the temple itself, the second group catered to visitors, and the lowest class lived on the temple grounds and were required to scour for customers in the Uruk city streets. It's relatively safe to assume that the Priests of Uruk, who presumably generated this idea of pious devotional prostitution, were all men. Innovative networking centres like the city of Uruk, also festered horrendous and abhorrent ideas, such as one of the most sinful, slavery.

Early hunter-gatherer tribes had little need or resources for slaves.[73] Their lifestyle, scarcity of food, and little division of labour often meant that the economic cost of maintaining a slave may have been more trouble than it was worth. It was the growth of agricultural abundance and the resulting social stratification, enabled by the idea of a settlement perfected in a city, that potentially encouraged humans to embrace the idea of subjugating other humans for their advantage. Sadly, it has been a plague on human society that we have been unable to purge ever since.

The slaves of Uruk were primarily accrued as a result of conquest and domination and were then used to assist with the ongoing construction of a business or the city. An individual, however, could also volunteer to be drafted into slavery if they could not pay a debt. Slaves in this period were household property and could be bought, inherited, or gifted into marriage. Slaves were often branded or pierced to display their lowly status and ownership. A middle-class citizen of Uruk may have held five people in their possession. The elite of the city may have had acquired up to one hundred souls bonded to them for life.[74] The preceding ideas of social status and materialism ultimately created the idea that the newly conquered, or poorest of people, could be considered as material property, similar to cattle or goats.

The mental algorithms of the rulers of these early cities concluded, from their perspective, that slavery was a terrific idea to help both construct and organise their city. This is despite this being such a rare and horrific condition, that it's rarely inflicted anywhere in the animal kingdom outside of scavenger ants.[75] There is also no confirmed analogy for slavery anywhere in the primate world, which indicates that slavery is another uniquely human idea and cannot be blamed on a recessive mammalian genetic instinct or impulse. It's our original idea. Worse still, it is an idea that humans have desperately clung to like a junkie returning to a disposable needle.

Despite being invented around 5,000 BC, slavery has tenaciously survived as an incredibly lucrative industry for many millennia. Especially during the 16th Century, when the "New World" of the Americas needed to be colonised for imperial economic gain, and nearly 12 million innocent African people were stolen into enforced perpetual bondage for over 300 years.[76] The perpetrators even used the sermons of the Old Testament to defend their disgusting ideas, suggesting that somehow God had given them his or her prior approval, a few thousand years before they committed their own devilish acts.[77]

Aeons after the clay walls of Uruk, that were also likely built by slaves, had crumbled into dust, wars over the idea of slavery were still being fiercely fought. In March 1865, the then US President, Abraham Lincoln, perfectly articulated how hideously myopic the idea of slavery is when he argued, "Whenever I hear anyone arguing for slavery, I feel a strong impulse to see it tried on him personally."[78] Twenty-nine days after making this public statement, he was assassinated by a bullet to the head partly due to his robust stance against slavery.[79] Despite the United States subsequently passing laws to abolish slavery in December 1865, it is estimated that even today, over 40 million fellow humans are currently quashed by this appalling exploitation of labour, sex or, marriage somewhere in the world.[80] Unfortunately, some of the very worst ideas cultivated in Uruk, live on in our society like radioactive cockroaches.

While our species has made pathetically slow progress on universally rejecting the idea of slavery, unfortunately, the slave-trade is still booming. According to investigative journalist, Kate Hodal, global slavery still generates as much as US$150 billion in annual profits. More than the annual profits of Apple and Amazon combined. Whereas 18th-century slave-traders were forced to contend with costly journeys and high mortality rates, modern exploiters have "benefitted" from lower overheads due to huge advances in transportation. Leveraging new ideas and technologies, modern slave-traders may now obscenely earn up to thirty times more than their 18th-century counterparts.[81] The fact that the world opinion now agrees that slavery is a morally wrong idea, does not eliminate the fact that millions of people habitually, and knowingly, act otherwise and wilfully profit in this idea daily.

Even with an idea as indefensible as slavery, there is no universal human mechanism, motivation, or agreement to deselect it as an option when economic and materialistic advances are to be made. If after 7,000 years of civilisation, elements of humanity are still actively pursuing ideas like slavery, what does this say about our global mental algorithms' ability to discern the good ideas from, not just the bad, but the disgusting? As a species, we often choose ideas that are game-changing, brilliantly disruptive, and intoxicatingly beautiful. Paradoxically, we are also continually exploiting ideas that are repugnant and repetitively immoral, when it suits our selfish motivations. Can we, as a species, be trusted with the very ideas we have created when each subsequent human generation is generating increasingly powerful, impactful, and potentially devastating ideas? Can we be sure that we won't select ideas on a selfish, materialistic, and short-term nature in defiance of the long-term prospects of our planet and species?

CHAPTER 4

THE IDEA HIVES.

Uruk was a relatively crude and gritty prototype designed to ferment people and ideas, at a scale never previously imagined, to generate new outcomes for survival. An early, yet important, human experiment in cultural innovation and critically, a society designed to create prosperity, safety, stability, and economic advantage for its citizens. Perhaps an unplanned outcome from the world's first "start-up city", is that it became a hive for creating collaborative ideas. A beta-trial that they continuously updated and reloaded for over 3,000 years before their mighty sandstone Ziggurats bled back into the sand. Eventually, their city crumbled, and their multi-generational experiment in innovation came to a whispering end. If it was not for their beautiful preserved clay tablets, their wondrous advances, innovations, and escapades might be as fabled as Plato's Atlantis.

Conquest and a changing climate played a role in Uruk's decline, and the last inhabitants left Uruk forever in 630 AD.[82] By that time, their idea of a "city" had well and truly spread globally, with centres like Rome, Constantinople (Istanbul) and Daxing (Beijing) taking the basic Uruk concept to much higher levels of scale, stability, security, and innovation that could never have been imagined by the early originators.

In the thousands of years since this early experiment, humans have dramatically expanded upon the core idea of a city. Parallel to this, we have also seen a progressive shift to where the majority of new ideas are now gestated within city structures. At the dawn of civilisation, new ideas would have originated from the relatively small, nomadic tribes of hunters and gatherers. Following this, agricultural villages would have staked their claim as the main hub for ideas, perhaps as early as 10,000 BC.[83] The concept of the "city" then evolved as the epicentre for human ideas and is now unlikely to ever yield its crown without a major cataclysm intervening. It is estimated that there are now 10,000 cities in the world, and this figure is still aggressively advancing. In fact, around half of today's cities did not even exist on Earth a mere forty years ago.[84]

To put this relentless urban acceleration into context, humanity added a pitiful one additional city to the planet every year, in the period between the Uruk's erecting their city walls in 4000 BC, and Pink Floyd releasing "Another Brick In The Wall" on vinyl in 1980 AD. Incredibly, since Roger Waters penned his rock masterpiece, humanity has aggressively stamped an unbelievable average of 125 new cities every year onto the surface of the Earth. If cities are truly hubs for increasing the probability of new ideas, and if each additional city generates even a small proportional quantity of additional ideas, then we are now entering into an unmatched period of human history where there will be an exponential deluge in the amount of new ideas offered to our species for evaluation, adoption, and even rejection.

The quantity, pace, and diversity of ideas that will fire-hose out of our cities over the coming decades, will be nothing like humanity has previously encountered. It may even be more than a single generation can potentially even evaluate. It is unclear whether humanity has either the bandwidth or the mind-space to successfully tackle the sheer volume of this emerging intellectual challenge of sorting the cascading good ideas from the socially destructive ones. It has never been attempted at this speed and scale in human history before. It is also probable that the ideas we will all be assessing will become progressively more impactful as our technology becomes increasingly powerful. That impact may be beautifully positive or destructively negative. It depends upon both the idea, and our decisions on how to deploy the idea. Humanity is no longer experimenting with chipped stone tools, but is playing with unparalleled sociological and networked technological fire.

As a signal of this rapid development, patents, as a proxy for new ideas, are now predominately hatched in cities, and there is an apparent and positive correlation between urban density and innovation.[85] This appears to build upon the legacy of the Uruk prototype as a vibrant hive to cultivate new ideas. In 2019, new patent applications in the United States, reached an all-time record of 669,434. That's over 1,800 new patents applied for every single day. For comparison, in 1970 at the very beginning of the documented recent acceleration of city development, there was just 109,539 patent applications during the entire year. That's an annual increase of 600% of patents for new ideas in the last fifty years.[86] Considering the first ever patent was lodged in 1421[87], and by 1921 USA patents were only 81,915[88] per year, there had been only modest growth in those past five hundred years. For anyone keeping score, China, in 2019, lodged over 1.4 Million patent applications, more than double the USA. It gives a strong indication to where the future of ideas are now streaming from.[89]

The ever-increasing human population, combined with the collaborative tools, capital, and urban city environments, has contributed to this exponential increase in patentable ideas. Humanity is not simply a passive witness to this increase, but desperately needs to actively assimilate and evaluate this explosion of new ideas that was unimaginable even forty years ago, let alone by our innovative ancestors in Uruk. Ideas can, and undoubtedly will, accelerate incredibly faster from here. They show no signs of stopping or abating. In comparison, the random ideas spun by genetic evolution relied on a patient, slow creep through time to assess their merit, and to remain on Earth through a prospering gene pool. This unfathomable length of time means that evolutionary changes play out across many generations. This is not so with human ideas, which can change the course of multiple species within the blink of a single generation.

Today, we devoutly worship at the alter of ideas emanating from the major centres of innovation such as Silicon Valley, Israel, Singapore, New York, Beijing, Austin, London, and Tokyo. These, and other key cities, provide the dynamic, random, and rich connections, as well as the specialisation, adjacency, and capital required to exponentially generate new ideas, that are ultimately worth patenting. This leaves the more isolated and disconnected rural communities, which also compete for talent, resources, tax breaks, and capital, at a relative commercial disadvantage when creating new ideas. Although advances in broadband communication, distributed workforces, and collaboration technology, may eventually help level the playing field between urban and rural idea creation opportunities.

However, as it currently stands, humanity seems irrevocably skewed towards continually focussing more resources on the mega-urban centres that we have deliberately engineered, celebrated, and invested in. Tokyo is the world's largest city with a hive-mind of 37 million inhabitants, followed by New Delhi with 29 million, Shanghai with 26 million, and Mexico City and São Paulo, each hold around 22 million movers, shakers, lovers, and beggars.[90] We have taken Uruk's fledgling beta-city concept of 10,000 people and exploded it into what is now a global urban population of over 4.2 billion people, which is expected to reach 6.7 billion people by 2050.[91]

Cities are almost, by default, designed to be idea machines. Not only because of the dense concentration of people, but because of the the opportunity and proximity for collaboration in a city environment. Educated and specialist trained minds are often placed adjacent to other trained minds in both planned and spontaneous ways. This diverse interaction delivers random, structured, and fresh experiences to the citizens which, in turn, generates new ideas. There apparently is a "Goldilocks" zone that optimises idea generation in a city. Like all systems, cities apparently have ideal operating parameters. Too few people and there is not enough feedback or interaction to generate new sparks. Too many people, and feedback turns into a blanket of noise, our creativity seems less able to break through the clutter, and it typically declines in effectiveness or drowns amongst a sea of unproductive chatter. This may be one of the reasons that it is the relatively lower density cities, and not the megacities, that account for the bulk of newly patented ideas.

Evidence for this comes from the fact that nearly three-quarters of all patents now come from urban locations that have a population density below 1,400 people per square km.[92] This is the approximate density of a centre like Palo Alto in USA. For comparison, Dhaka, the most densely populated city in the world, has over thirty times this level, with almost 45,000 people per square km.[93] Similarly, in tandem with innovation, happiness of the citizens in a city also tends to decline when urban density increases beyond a certain point.[94] As the economic development of a city rises, psychological well-being follows, however, it eventually reaches an inflection point, after which dissatisfaction increases, no matter what the underlying wealth of the population becomes. Endless growth, it seems, does not constantly equate to more ideas, better ideas, and more happiness. Despite this fact, many major companies, politicians, and economists all consistently embrace the idea and panacea of planet-wide "growth" as a seemingly borderless journey to the promised land of civilisation perfection. This nirvana is unlikely to be reached as the idea of "more" as a defining strategy is rarely an optimal long-term outcome for a person, city, state, empire, or any operating system.

There may well be a myriad of interconnected and underlying economic, social, and structural issues that help propel this phenomenon of declining happiness in escalating urban environments. Perhaps a rapidly emerging element that especially challenges humanity's ability to endlessly prosper in this expansive environment, may now simply be a superfluous abundance of choice; a natural outcome from the ocean of ideas generated by our mega-cities.

The leading American Psychologist, Barry Schwartz, has established an incredibly compelling theory that more choice paradoxically leads to a paralysis of decisions, and indeed increased unhappiness, rather than contentment.[95] A range of ideas, once clearly articulated and shared within a society, then become implicit choices that we need to actively make. Ideas are opportunities to ignore, follow, or retreat from a choice. A new pool of ideas are simply choices that we all need to engage with on a daily basis. We must use our mental algorithms, based on our intellect and experiences, to determine whether we should manifest an idea into reality, or allow it to be snapped out of existence. Like a child in a candy store, it may appear that the more choices we are presented with, the happier we will be, but according to research from Professor Schwartz, this is merely an illusion.

The argument is that our psyche overloads when presented with a gluttony of choice. All computational systems, like algorithms and programs, are designed to have ideal operating parameters. The human brain is no different. It has evolved to receive data from our senses, process information, and filter choices to determine what ideas would optimise the best prospects for individual survival. When presented with too many ideas, or too much data, this can lead to a paralysis of decision making. If we then make an active decision, in the presence of too much choice, we subsequently become increasingly dissatisfied with our selected option. With too many options, our brains begin to second guess whether we have made the correct choice, or whether a better choice was left hidden in the pack. People, when presented with a large flock of ideas, and forced to select just one to hold in their hands, uncontrollably and subconsciously yearn over the other ideas that they left behind. More choice in ideas does not mean more happiness, and yet we are living in a period with exponential global growth in the amount of choices we suddenly have when selecting ideas.

Professor Schwartz argues that we all share this experience every day. For example, enter any restaurant and read the menu. Faced with too many meal choices, we assume that the chef has not applied the appropriate care to select, craft, or curate the quality of our food. We may then consider all the menu items to be produced with the flavour and consistency of Turkish prison meatloaf. Too few menu choices, and we suspect that our discerning taste buds have been unjustly restricted from the opportunity of delight, and we feel constrained. His research indicates that the satisfaction with our food choice declines in both instances, and that we are programmed to optimal satisfaction when the choices given are not too few and importantly, not too many.

Professor John Edwards at Bournemouth University has studied this apparent dichotomy. It appears that the optimal amount of choice on a restaurant menu is seven starters, ten mains, and then seven desserts. Any significant deviation from this and it can negatively affect the psychology of our dinning experience.[96] We either feel that there is too little choice, or far too much. A significant variance from this optimum doesn't sit well with how our intellect is designed to assess a range of ideas. Our decision-making ability has evolved to operate optimally in a defined window where we desire to have a manageable amount of ideas to first assess and select from, but not too many, or it may seed confusion and germinate disappointment. Scale this concept beyond the setting of a restaurant into the broader context of the constant interactions in modern civilisation, and it can be argued that the urbanisation of mankind and the social media proliferation of ideas has created the largest menu of choices in history. People are now continually required to swipe through this endlessly scrolling menu to find the happiness needle amongst the exponential idea haystack.

An excessive buffet of idea choices is being spread within our civilisation on a daily basis through our cities, feeds, phones, screens, and personal interactions. The list of all available human ideas has continued to accelerate since the Uruk's invented "The City", and these veritable idea-hives are now expanding at a rate unparalleled in human experience. However, our brain's underlying physiology and processing ability does not conform to the robotic increase in computational power predicted by "Moores Law".[97] Unlike the engineered silicon transistors we have created, our brains can't double in processing power every two years to keep pace with this exploding cacophony of choice that now soaks into every aspect of our society.

Our minds may therefore be in a constant psychological struggle to maintain the balance between the myriad of daily decisions we must quickly synthesise to prosper and progress, and our evolved desire to limit total input to maintain happiness and stability. The relentless drum of new ideas, driven by the unparalleled urbanisation and population growth, may now be pushing our species closer to the brink of Professor Schwartz's "paralysis of choice." We may need to be presented with less ideas, instead of more, to be happier with our choices and have increased confidence to make the right ones. Unnervingly, some of the latest technological ideas specifically designed to propel ideas between people and continents with increasing speed, pervasiveness, and algorithmic predictability, could be a catalyst that pushes some people towards this state of psychological imbalance. We are all not only compelled to make more choices, but the pace of which they are presented to us is now nearing the speed of light. This onslaught is also a relatively new experience for the human psyche to grapple with. As both the volume and pace of idea generation explodes, it may lead pockets of our society into this "paralysis of choice".

In 522 BC, Darius The Great was crowned King of all Persia at the wise age of 28. By his own account, he was proclaimed King over five other worthy contenders, when the noble horse he was seated on was the very first to "whinny" at the sight of the rising sun. This signalled that he was touched by the Gods, and thus, had the divine right to rule above all others.[98] He later admitted that his personal groom, Oebares, had secretly rubbed his hand over the moist genitals of a nearby mare. While the other contenders gazed expectantly East towards the sunrise, Oebares, slyly touched the reigns of Darius' heroic stallion, allowing it to briefly marinate in the mare's scent. The resulting excited neigh from Darius' stallion was, as a result, less the trumpeting of a heavenly angel, but the snort of a horny horse. A cunningly good idea if you want to be anointed as a King by the Gods and minimise the chances that the Gods may actually share their point of view, and select one of your competitors.

Darius The Great, had a number of other great ideas during his reign. His main idea was to dominate and subjugate as much of the known world as he possibly could. By the time he was done, in 486 BC, his empire covered Mesopotamia, Egypt, Anatolia, Arabia, and even Libya. At its peak, over 40% of the world's known population was under the rule of his royal thumb.

Driven by necessity, he had the vision to create a ground-breaking and innovative method to broadcast his commands across his vast empire. He called his revolutionary idea "The Angarium".[99] This was the world's first system of co-ordinated horse riders, designed to rapidly transfer messages along the Royal Road, which he commissioned to transverse the length of his Kingdom. A messenger on foot would have taken up to ninety days to travel 2,700km starting in Susa (in modern day in Iran) to the Port of Smyrna, on the Aegean Sea (in modern day Turkey). With the advent of the Angarium, this journey could now be achieved in only nine days. A remarkable leap forward in the spread of information across large distances. It increased the speed of transmission of ideas ten fold. The Greek historian, Herodotus, was in awe of Darius' invention of the Angarium, remarking in 440 BC, "there is nothing mortal which accomplishes a journey with more speed than these messengers, so skilfully has this been invented by the Persians."[100]

Herodotus was right. The Angarium was the 5G Internet of its day, and Darius was like a King Zuckerberg, managing all access to the content that could travel on the platform. This speed of information exchange stood unsurpassed for over two hundred years. It wasn't until the Chinese Emperor Qin Shi Huang started building the Great Wall, in 221 BC, that the race towards the information age received its first major upgrade. Utilising a series of up to 25,000 signal fires, strategically stationed at watch-towers along his impressive wall, a message could be passed over 1,000km in just a few hours.[101] This innovation succeed in giving Emperor Huang a competitive advantage in increasing stability and security against the invading Huns, hunkered on the other side of the wall. Ever since this innovation, mankind has been on an unquenched and continuous race to accelerate the circulation of information and ideas, with just two objectives in mind; more information and faster.

For the first few thousand years of human civilisation, the only true competitor to the Angarium for rapid information and idea exchange, involved a much smaller animal than a horse; the carrier pigeon. The initial genius of this "communication technology" may date back to as early as 2,900 BC[102] when a truly inquisitive and observant Egyptian realised that pigeons always returned to their home-base. Records indicate that ancient Egyptians would spread news of the anointment of a new Pharos via this medium. Additionally, the Maritime Empire of the Phoenicians may have released pigeons to communicate their trials and tribulations back to their homes from their expertly constructed ships as they traded across the Mediterranean Sea during 1,000 BC.

Whomever first had the idea to use a pigeon to transfer data, also selected them for their speed, as pigeons are incredibly fast and have impressive range. They can fly at an average speed of 77km per hour, and can travel up to 600km per day.[103] By the time the year 776 BC dawned, the carrier pigeon was still one of the leading technologies employed by the ancient Greeks to broadcast social news on important events, such as the inaugural winner of their very first Olympic Games. Spoiler alert, the winner of the only event in these Games, a 192 meter running race, was a very swift chef called Coroebus of Elis.[104] The Roman Emperor, Julius Cesar, also used carrier pigeons to communicate strategic battle ideas with his leaders in Gaul (France) around 50 BC.[105]

The use of pigeons, as an idea and information exchange network, dominated the planet for speed and efficacy for thousands of years. Even the rabid conquer, Genghis Kahn, leveraged their innate skills to orchestrate idea-exchange across his vast empire in circa 1,200 AD.[106]

Presumably, some of his lightly laden pigeons transported the ideas of his secret innovations, as he was the very first person in history to use gunpowder to create grenades as a weapon in battle.[107]

Compared to how consumers are now trained to salivate at the monotonous metronome of Apple's newest release of communication innovations, the ancient world had to wait many generations for any breakthrough in new communication ideas. To illustrate this, even after almost 5,000 years of progressive innovation, during the chaos of World War I, the carrier pigeon was still used as instrumental technology for communication. The British Army enlisted around 12,000 carrier pigeons to transmit messages during the Battle of the Somme in 1916.[108] The US Army Signal Core also had a "fleet" of 600 carrier pigeons stationed in France during the same period. They were so critical for the co-ordination of Army information that one of them, a brave pigeon named "Cher Ami", was awarded a prestigious French medal, the «Croix de Guerre", for desperately delivering a message after being badly wounded under-fire. This information saved the lives of 194 US soldiers. In 1931, Cher Ami was inducted in the now bygone "Pigeon Hall of Fame".[109] Pigeon fanciers around the world should not despair, however, at the fall from prominence of these prized birds. It has been recently reported that terrorist organisations are still utilising this ancient technology to share their evil ideas while attempting to stay off the data-driven grid.[110]

For millennia, the best ideas of the human race were exchanged between cities and civilisations by either signal fire, drum, smoke signals, saddled riders, ships, or pigeons. These technologies were all extremely limited in speed, and what we might now call, bandwidth of exchange. This means that any new effervescent idea created in these burgeoning cities, were relatively slow to spread and socialise to other "idea hives" by today's standards. Cities were operating like archipelagos of information islands that were only loosely connected across a vast ocean. Innovations created in these idea-hives, leaked out comparatively slowly. The content that dripped from them was often controlled by the those in power, as they simultaneously controlled the message and the means of exchange, be it rider, ship, or pigeon. For thousands of years, the transmission of both knowledge and ideas was often skewed towards specific regions, a specific economic class, or industry. It was not democratised or unleashed to be in the hands of the general population to share ideas of their own.

Importantly, the spread of ideas was also limited in total volume as well. Ancient scrolls, skins, clay tablets, and handwritten books contained important knowledge, as well as state, and religious ideas. These were mostly stored in important libraries, palaces, or churches but were limited in quantity given the time, skill, and effort required in both production and storage.[111] Moveable-type printing, a corner-stone for the mass-production of modern books, was first invented by the Chinese Artisan, Bi Sheng in 1,000 AD. This subsequently created an environment where printed books became symbols of status and wealth amongst the elite in China. To illustrate how slowly ideas evolved and spread in this environment, Europeans waited another 450 years before Joannes Guttenburg began working on his own revolutionary printing press using movable metal-type to print with greater speed, volume, and precision. This long delay is despite the relative simplicity of creating type for a latin alphabet compared to the complexity of Chinese characters.

Guttenburg's innovation was another vital step in the journey of communication and idea exchange, that the Sumerians began 6,000 years earlier with their carved clay tablets. The expansion and economies of printing, meant that the process of idea sharing was no longer limited to the ancient craft of story-telling, and written content was suddenly not exclusively controlled by the elite.[112] It was one of the key advancements that helped to liberate ideas from the satellites of individual cities, so they could slowly spread their beautiful and inspiring tentacles across the globe.

The true inflection point on the path to transmit humanity's ideas with unlimited speed, reach, and volume was only turned-on in the mid-Nineteenth Century by two perspicuous inventors. Samuel Morse, who pioneered wired communication, and Guglielmo Marconi, who created the early breakthroughs in wireless communication.

Morse had the foresight to imagine relays, that enable electronic signals to be sent along a wire further than ever before, and thus, giving potential to create long-distance electronic communication. In 1842, he proved this concept to the US Congress when he transmitted messages between two committee rooms that he had wired in the Capital Building. Impressed, they supported him with a grant for US$30,000 to develop his idea for electronic messaging. By 1845, he founded the Magnetic Telegraphy Company, and within five years, over 12,000 miles of wire buzzed between Boston, New York, Washington, and other key "idea hives" in the USA.[113] At the time, his invention was limited to the equivalent of thirty characters per minute, much less that a tweet.[114] Even with this meagre volume, the change in speed of data flow was enough to be world-changing. In 1852 it took twelve days to send a letter from London to New York and seventy-three days to get all the way under to Australia.[115] The Telegraph changed this forever as ideas could be rapidly exchanged without the limitations of speed and distance.

By 1866, the Atlantic Telegraph Company laid commercial submarine cables across the ocean, and information could be seamlessly exchanged across continents for the first time in history.[116] The second great idea that Mr Morse was involved in, was the famous code that still bears his name. The iconic series of dots and dashes, globally adopted to enable telegraph operators to translate the squawking electric pulses into letters, news, instructions, ideas, and poetry. Although, it must be noted that not all of his ideas were good ones. It is widely reported that Mr Morse was decidedly pro-slavery and believed that the subjugation of people against their will was part of God's divine plan.[117]

As important as an idea that the Telegraph was, it had one key limitation. The process of building a global network of cables. To connect the continents and key cities of the world was expensive and time-consuming to build and maintain. What the world needed was a way to rapidly share ideas across vast distances without the inconvenience of wires or the distinct physical limitations of even the most robust pigeon.

By the time Marconi was born in 1874 into Italian Nobility, the twisted cables of telegraphy already had criss-crossed the globe. He was fascinated by electricity and engineering, and from an early age, experimented with technology at his home. At the age of 20, inspired by the work on electromagnetic radiation by the German engineer, Heinrich Hertz, he began trying to leverage "Hertzian" waves for communication purposes. In 1895, he developed a prototype system that could transmit a signal via radio waves, up to two miles across the picturesque Italian countryside.[118] Realising this was an astounding breakthrough, he knew he needed capital to scale his idea. Unable to secure funds in Italy, he travelled to the United Kingdom, and in 1896 gained support for his innovation by pitching it to the British Post Office, Navy, and Army.

Backed by their commitments, he formed The Wireless Telegraph and Signal Company, and by 1901 he had succeed with the very first transatlantic "wireless" message crossing thousands of miles between Britain and Canada.[119] The message was short, just three Morse code "dots" that signified the letter "S", however, the future implications for humanity was massive. From this point onwards, our ideas were unleashed to effortlessly travel the world with freedom and impunity. Ideas were destined to be unlocked and liberated at a speed and scale undreamed of by early innovators in information exchange, like Darius The Great, or Emperor Huang.

Today, little more than one hundred years after Marconi's breakthrough (and many rapid, incredible, iterative technological innovations later) our society now takes for granted the fact that we can globally share an unlimited amount of ideas with a click or a swipe at the speed of light, using the powerful platforms of the internet and wireless broadband communication. The spread of ideas is no longer significantly limited in either volume or geography. The amount of data that now sits behind all of our exchanges is unfathomably large.

Accordingly to current estimates, the total digital universe is now approximately 44 zettabytes. This is forty times more digital bytes than there are stars in the observable universe.[120] In a period of 7,000 years, since people first created the concept of "The City" which concentrated interactions and generated innovations, it has now been scaled to where we now dominate the planet and can connect with everyone, both physically and virtually, so that ideas can effortlessly flow between these hubs. This level of technological advancement, in both idea exchange and storage, is now enabling the entire sprawling bait-ball of human ideas, to float in the internet and be distributed, without friction, instantly across the planet. Our very best ideas, and all of our bad ones, are now immediately available anywhere and everywhere. Flooding not just social media feeds, but submerging senses as well. This may also effect our ability to skilfully wade through them all using our mental algorithms, evolved to deal with a dramatically different level of input, data and choices. We now live in a technological idea-restaurant, with an unlimited menu, offering millions of choices. This may be compounding towards a "paralysis of choice" or simply increasing the dissatisfaction with the choices we eventually do make. This may be due to the fact that, while our ideas have evolved, the hardware that humanity operates on, our psychology and physiology, has been relatively static.

With over 4.5 billion people now online[121] and with 3.9 billion of us routinely engaged in social media[122], the sheer pace of idea exchange has frenetically increased and the total digital cacophony of them is arguably, becoming deafening. Every day, Facebook users post 350 million photos, there are 500 million tweets[123], while YouTube-watchers slack-jaw for a total of 1 billion hours.[124] Each year, there are trillions of new ideas emailed, tweeted, and shared that humans need to decide whether to engage with or not. Many ideas are so trivial that they require minimal attention. Some, however, may be important to the future of an individual, a town, or even a country. How do we filter the good and the bad from the obese circulating whale of the downright ugly and inflammatory ideas? No matter how the Everest of social media statistics are sliced and diced, two facts will consistently emerge. Social-media interactions are unimaginably immense, and are still escalating at a glutinous volume. Short of a massive comet kissing the Earth, there is no way of easily putting this loquacious communication genie back in its bottle. Our ideas have been unleashed, like a turbulent tsunami hitting a shoreline, and it is our minds and senses that it's constantly washing over.

The original design for a city optimised collaboration inside the walls, but delivered protection and security from invasion outside it. The infrastructure and accessibility of the internet has created connections at a scale that dwarfs even the largest mega-cities in the world, and in the process, is breaking down any protection that a city wall would have offered from invading ideas. We have now assembled a massive, interconnected "virtual city", totalling an online potential of 4.6 billion people. A planet sized community, that no longer requires the necessity of physicality and proximity for its citizens to be intimately and instantly adjacent to exchange thoughts, concepts, lies, pornography, and profanity. This can be beautiful, but it can also be bulimic. Even language is rapidly disappearing as an impediment for idea exchange as instantaneous machine-translation continues to grow in efficiency.[125]

We are building and feeding a gigantic virtual crucible of ideas. It took 7,000 years to gradually evolve from an idea-hive of 10,000 people hunkered in Uruk to a virtual mega-hive of 4.6 billion people connected across the cities, towns, and villages around the world. In addition to this, by 2030, it is estimated that there will be 50 billon devices connected to this same virtual hive as the "Internet of Things" continues to develop. These devices will be constantly feeding their own data, information and insights into the system which, in many cases, will stimulate further discussions, options and thoughts that people will pile on top of their ever-expanding digital slag heap.

As a species, we evolved in an environment where we had both time and space to absorb and manage the collective data of our daily reality.

The pace of change was relatively slow and the volume of accessible ideas was comparably small. The data explosion over the past fifty years, would blow the minds of the original inhabitants of Uruk. The speed and volume of the internet takes their original idea of a city as an idea hub, into nuclear overdrive. What would Herodotus now say (or tweet) about our 21st century version of the Angarium? Our technology is now evolving faster than any genetic revolution could ever do.

We should ask ourselves, is our society, psychology and biology prepared to synthesise and select the best from this growing onslaught of ideas? The most ideas that the world has ever seen, evolving in the space of a few generations. The entrepreneur and innovator, Steve Jobs once proclaimed "innovation is saying no to a thousand things."[126] The challenge now for all of us is this; how do we say no to a thousand things when there are a million new things arriving in our feeds everyday? They need to be assessed and reviewed before being discarded. Are we still the fittest species to make these choices in this environment, or do we need to urgently change, adapt, or evolve to catch up with the insanity of our ideas?

CHAPTER 5

THE DOPAMINE APES.

Thank you for reading this far and taking the plunge into ideas. Research shows that only 19% of adults actively read on a daily basis, and most for a measly seven minutes. In fact, 24% of Americans state that they haven't bothered to read a book in the last year[127], while the average Netflix viewer manages to squeeze in two hours of content on their couch every day.[128] Congratulations, this means that you are part of an elite group of readers and should feel positive about your commitment.

If you truly believe the compliment in the preceding paragraph, you probably received a small jolt of the chemical "dopamine" into your brain as part of your naturally evolved and complex chemical reward mechanism. It is a neurotransmitter released into our brains to help promote positive behaviour, and increase the likelihood of repeat behaviour. It may also simply reinforce the pleasure principle, in other words, making the good feel really, really good. From a pharmacological perspective, dopamine both anticipates and rewards outcomes. Therefore, besides pleasure, it influences our motivations and emotions both pre and post the decision to act. As an example, imagine the feeling of anticipation when a chrome ball bounces and spins above the numbered pockets on a roulette wheel after placing a sizeable bet. This feeling can be the rush of a dopamine response. Whether we win or lose, our brains can be stimulated by the activity alone, regardless of the result.

Dopamine is what feeds the Pavlov's dog that barks in our brain. It's the compound that makes us sit up and beg, and also believe that we are good dogs for doing so. It's instant, addictive, uncontrollable, and it deliberately feeds our ego every day. Dopamine was designed by evolution to help optimise and memorise survival strategies like sex, food, sociability, and generally encourage the right choices to live better and longer. While other mammals emit the same compounds, none do so quite like human beings.[129] It helps the brain reinforce, and then repeat, the positive behaviour we have discovered or learned. Dopamine production in the brain is associated with music, learning, gambling, food, social interaction, love, orgasms, and acceptance. It, therefore, plays an important role in idea selection. Faced with a choice of ideas, selecting one and having a positive response from that selection, means that dopamine may play a role in helping to promote the same selection in the future. It works perfectly for shaping and reinforcing survival strategies for our species, until we artificially manipulate it, and then it doesn't.

Cocaine, for example, has an elegant dance with dopamine.[130] The normal chemical release of dopamine takes the form of a synchronised relay race. It travels through our brain elegantly from neurone to neurone like a charging Angarium rider, passing messages through ancient Persia by traveling from station to station. A line of cocaine subversively blocks this dopamine rider. It creates an artificial traffic jam at the neurone, which then forces dopamine to accumulate at the synapse. It builds up, and in the process, imparts a delusional state of euphoria in the brain. It's one of the reasons that some drugs become so addictive, as they distort our brain's mesolimbic dopamine system, and fools our reward systems. This naturally positive chemical messenger, designed to promote good choices and behaviour, when over-stimulated, can actually cause system-wide destruction and chaos. Although Charlie Sheen might strongly disagree.

Over time, evolution slowly, carefully, and precisely designed dopamine release specifically for bi-pedal apes that banded together in small groups, with presumably relatively limited daily interactions compared to our modern urban society. A dopamine shot for a positive action within these ancient tribes, may have beautifully promoted behaviour to preserve the harmony, safety, and security of the individual or perhaps, even the tribe itself. The delicate neurochemistry that slowly evolved to trigger these vitally important behaviours that differentiate us from other early hominids, may date back as far as 4.4 million years.[131]

Unfortunately, evolution was not necessarily engineering this chemical reward system to take into consideration that our sub-consciously operated dopamine response system would eventually need to deal with stimulation in multiple forms and artificial sources. Not only from the intense excesses of Pablo Escobar's finest export, but increasingly from the overdose of a billion social interactions from a Tik-Toking, Instagramming, Twittering interactive screen becoming glued to our Kardashian-seeking, Clockwork-Orange eyeballs, twenty-four hours a day. Recent Harvard research has indicated that every social click, like, tweet, mention, and share we receive or anticipate receiving, juices our dopamine levels just a little bit higher.[132] The impact of our technological ideas is that they are increasingly stimulating our reward systems in a manner that our biology wasn't specifically evolved for. Many social media algorithms are seemingly aware that a consequence of their product is to squirt more dopamine into our system, and increases the probability of repetitive and sticky behaviour. Some may even be engineered to monetise it by maximising attention and loyalty through constantly modelling and rewarding consumer motivations and behaviour.[133]

Abraham Maslow was born in Brooklyn as a son of Ukrainian Jewish immigrants. In 1943, as a Professor of Psychology at Brooklyn College in the University of New York, it is likely that the horrendous atrocities of Nazism against the Jewish population in Europe, both disgusted and plagued his mind professionally and personally, given his background and beliefs. As a psychologist, he wanted to articulate how the human mind functioned and made choices. Good, bad, and even horrific ones. To his eye, Sigmund Freud's robotic stimulus and response architecture of human behaviour did not resonate completely. He believed that there was more subtlety, complexity, and depth to the human psyche then just a DNA gum-ball machine, acting on pre-programmed instincts and responses. As the war raged in Europe, he announced his theory of human motivation as a Hierarchy.[134] Visually represented as a pyramid, it appears to build upon each layer as if the Pharaoh Khufu erected it from blocks of immutable limestone. Maslow understood that mankind was more fluid than this structure conveyed. His "Hierarchy of Needs" was not to be seen as a rigid ladder to climb, but more as an interconnected web of filters buried deep within our synapses. This is where our ideas, choices, and decisions are shuffled, considered, jumbled, and then judged before we enact them into reality. Maslow's hierarchy of mental filters covers the full gamut of our impulses, emotions, fears, relationships, creativity, ego, physiology, morality, and even spirituality. Our genes, environment, subconscious, and life experiences constantly adjust these mental filters to help govern our decisions. Our individual, complex, and often, opaque mental algorithms, are what makes humanity both predictable and deliciously random, when it comes to selecting ideas to follow. The fingerprint-like diversity of a person's mental filters means that different people can look at the exact same idea and arrive at completely divergent conclusions, as to its merits. Any objective facts used to support ideas are always subjectively assessed by the complex mental filters of each individual. As a result, defining an objectively good idea is exceedingly difficult, as no two people will have identical mental filters to judge the quality of the idea. Their religion, experiences, beliefs, ego, emotions, fears, biases, needs, and many other subtle parameters will skew the perceptions and acceptance of any given idea. A good idea is, unfortunately, often only in the mind of the beholder.

Maslow's Hierarchy of Needs is, however, merely an approximation of human motivations and not an etched blueprint or a rulebook to be blindly followed. This model, and many others that have been subsequently proposed, are often only a crude, analogue approximation for predicting human behaviour and idea selection. The broad parameters may be insightful, but models can be devoid of the essential real-time personal data to be truly meaningful as a precise and predictive tool. Maslow designed his model for a theoretical offline world, and not as a GPS tracker for the mind. It is a holistic framework for humanity that lacks the laser-guided insight of a smart-bomb to calculate how an individual would judge an idea in a particular context.

As blunt as it may have been, for over fifty years it was one of the benchmark ideas on how individual people made choices. However, not any longer. The latest data driven ideas on targeting individual behaviour makes Maslow's model look as fit as a field mouse in the Kentucky Derby. Over the last thirty years, the major industrial internet corporations, such as Google, Facebook, Amazon, Apple, Twitter, Alibaba, and TenCent, have been expanding their ability to predict human behaviour using the powerful idea of data driven digital algorithms. These are based upon a symbiosis of big data and highly segmented interaction profiles gleaned from multiple devices and constant interaction. On Facebook alone, every sixty seconds, 510,000 comments are posted, 293,000 statuses are updated, four million posts are liked, and 136,000 photos are uploaded.[135] The sheer volume of social data available to drive consumer insight is becoming biblical in scale, and insanely valuable to track and monetise.

From this Godzilla-quantity of consumer interactions, social media companies have the ability to instantly analyse and creatively cross-reference demographic, geographic, and psychographic information gathered on and outside of their platforms, as behaviour can be tracked long after people click away from a site. As social media and content companies curate an ever-increasing galaxy of data, they can also continuously deploy and fine-tune their algorithms to both anticipate and promote their desired consumer behaviour. Is it sometimes inaccurate and clumsy? Yes, but the leap forward in capability compared to the sparse data that Maslow had access to, is nothing short of transformative. The real question is how accurate and powerful it will grow to be at predicting and shaping behaviour in another fifty years, at the current pace of evolution?

These dominant internet platforms have become increasingly more powerful and valuable than Maslow ever dreamed of. In 2020, Google, Facebook, and Amazon earned US$64.4 billion in combined profit.[136] A significant amount of their success can be credited to how they expertly monetise their increasingly sophisticated, completely proprietary algorithms built on the endless flow of user-information and engineered to provide excruciatingly insightful information into the personal choices and behaviour of billions of people, for advertisers of all shapes and sizes.

A key element of creating astronomical value in the digital economy is having an ability to track and anticipate trillions of consumer decisions, to create powerful advertising platforms and sub-consciously influence consumers in a predetermined direction, to make consumers more predictable in their behaviour, and, therefore, increasingly valuable to advertisers and content producers. In the process, digital algorithms give priority to the content shown in social media feeds that maintains attention longer, or provokes a response from people to maximise engagement.

The completely involuntary response to what we see, feel, and hear in our social media streams, is often a small squirt of dopamine into our brains due to our ancient behaviour reward system.[137] Just as the gambler excitedly anticipates the next lucky number, our constant desire for likes, comments, posts, and retweets, fuels our attention and triggers our emotions. Our neural-chemistry automatically rewards our brains with drops of dopamine, and this can reinforce our behaviour to constantly return to the social media platform and repeat the desired actions. This mechanism can ultimately play an important commercial role in creating, managing and, monetising a digital eco-system.

In their published principles, Google suggests that their patented PageRank™ algorithm is enhanced by the democratisation of the internet, as the more open and accessible the available content is, the more importance can be ascribed to it by the "voting" population of millions or billions of people.[138] Therefore, the accuracy, potency, and value of their search products may be dependent on the freedom and openness of searchable information. Ensuring that people are constantly engaged with a platform may also be a key part of any algorithmic development, accuracy, and value creation.

The same can be true for a social media platform that also requires the constant fodder of data streams to be able to monetise their colossal customer bases through their highly segmented advertising services. It has been reported that Facebook collects up to 99% of its revenue from advertising, while Google makes 85%[139], and Twitter draws in around 86%.[140] For these types of platforms to maintain and competitively attract advertising revenue, it is critical that they have a high frequency and duration of consumer engagement, while simultaneously unleashing the tools to extract, manage, segment, and then sell the insights that come from the endless digital grazing by the online masses. Dopamine is the hidden chemical currency that can be exploited by platforms to encourage people to keep clicking for more.[141] The notion of whether social media is addictive was not completely embraced by leading social media platforms executives, when they appeared in front of the US Senate Judiciary Committee in 2020. Facebook CEO, Mark Zuckerberg, stated that the available data as to whether social media is addictive is "inconclusive", and he had not see any "internal research" that indicated it was. While Twitter CEO, Jack Dorsey, suggested that the tools could be addictive, like anything else that the consumers engage with.[142]

Many of the key social media platforms will, however, publicly and rightly support the concept of free speech to enable content, ideas, and opinions to flow openly across their platforms. In 2019, Mark Zuckerberg underscored the importance of this principle when he stated that, "People having the power to express themselves at scale is a new kind of force in the world."[143] In 2020, he reportedly reinforced his views on openness by suggesting, "I just believe strongly that Facebook shouldn't be the arbiter of truth of everything that people say online".[144] While many social media companies do have published policies and active programs designed to limit the content shared on their platforms, in areas such as decency and hate, the effectiveness of these policies is debatable, and their is no mechanism to ensure that they are defined and applied consistently across platforms, issues, and countries. There are new social platforms emerging in response to these initiatives, positioned to champion free-speech. One such example, is US based social application called "Parler" who encourages members to "Speak freely and express themselves openly, without fear of being "de-platformed" for their views."[145] Ironically, they themselves were "de-platformed" by Apple, Google, and Amazon in January 2021 after allegedly not moderating violent speech.[146]

Undoubtedly, a diametrically-opposed world where ideas are censored, edited, curtailed, or punished is not likely to lead to a more positive, balanced, or inclusive society either. Who would select the ideas for either amplification or deletion? On what basis, and on who's agenda? Free speech is the keystone of a healthy democracy and any single voice, company, or institution monopolising or controlling messaging, consistently builds pathways towards a darker totalitarian society. This is by no means a new idea. In 1786, Thomas Jefferson, one of the Founding Fathers of the United States, clearly articulated this when he wrote, "Our liberty depends on the freedom of the press, and that cannot be limited without being lost." [147] Ideas need to be forever free.

While "free-speech" is a vital component for both the sharing and generation of new ideas in a community, a nation, and around the world, it is not analogous to equal, balanced, fair, or truthful speech, when it comes to social media platforms. The reality is that not all free speech is shared and distributed in an equivalent manner, speed, or volume. Social media platforms are a business, and have a responsibility to their shareholders for profitability and growth. One key strategy is to maintain and grow engagement by designing algorithms that serve, suggest, and recommend content that will maximise the probability that people will continue watching, clicking, and commenting. These algorithms are highly sophisticated, constantly learning and have the ability to instantly tailor their recommendations to individuals based on highly predictive data driven analytics.

The engineered purpose of these algorithms is to digitally sieve through millions of possible content recommendations to find the most effective forms of the available pool of "free-speech" that will increase the probability of keeping people engaged on the platform. Unfortunately, the selected bytes of free-speech that are chosen by these powerful algorithms, can also be polarising, partisan, controversial, divisive, hateful, violent, deceitful and sometimes, complete and utter lies. This may happen because the algorithms intuitively understand that this type of content provokes a response from people, and the more it does, the more valuable it is, and, as a result, the more it will be served to consumers. It's like feeding an increasing amount of digital dung to to a planet of insatiable dung beetles. It's not necessarily the most appealing meal, but it is powerful in gaining their constant attention.

Algorithms are anticipatory, predictive, and, from a certain perspective, often made to be deliberately biased. Perhaps not in a traditional sense of politics, race, class, or ideology. Although these may be natural outcomes or manifestations of their actions. Instead, the content they select for consumers, are often engineered to be biased towards profitability by maximising engagement. Algorithms don't necessarily have independent morality. They coldly crunch the streams of data that stems from humanity, and then recommend videos, images and stories that they confidently predict will continue to press our hot buttons. The longer, more attentive, and more engaged a consumer is on any social platform, the more data they generate, the more predictable they will become, and the more value they are to advertisers and potential revenue streams. An algorithm may ultimately be inadvertently designed to keep all of humanity online and auto-playing the content for as long as possible, if that would maximise profit.

Tristan Harris, a leading advocate for social media reform, and the Co-Founder and President of the Center for Humane Technology[148] has been passionately shining a light on what he argues to be both a growing and alarming problem, potentially destructive to society. He alleges that misleading content is all too often amplified and shared at a massive scale by social media algorithms to maximise company value. He argues that "fake news spreads six times faster than true news because fake news and salacious ideas are more exciting, and more confirming of what we want to believe. And so we spread them immediately, before we actually ever get the correction."[149] Whether this misleading content is a Q-Anon video, a fraudulent election story, a flat earth conspiracy, or even a magic cure for a virus, they are all ideas in digital forms that have no virtual limitation on geographical expansion, as they capture attention, and provoke a response.

Misleading, inaccurate, provocative, and divisive ideas are now being amplified and scaled by pervasive global mediums while our ancient, neural-chemical, dopamine system, is constantly rewarding us for engaging with them. The content can cover a full spectrum of ideas including race, religion, nationalism, sexism, climate change, celebrities, economic disparity, tribalism, class systems, politics, health, viruses, enemies, and, of course, conspiracy theories and cat videos. Our species has consciously built a global 24x7, content delivery system that's is willing to constantly feed us provocative click-bait and even erroneous ideas, simply to make more money. We are in danger of becoming insatiable screen apes, releasing a dopamine banana every time we are triggered by a provocative video.

As pervasive and important broadcast TV was, up until the 1990s, it was always a relatively dumb medium. No instant interaction, no real-time data, no true personalised insight. A dunce tube, sitting remedially in the corner of the nation's living room. The data that digital media companies now massively absorb, provide them with the cookie-crumbs that leads us towards a more polarised world, where we become less objectively in control of the ideas we view, evaluate, and action.

The choice of ideas that we consume is being progressively subverted by these algorithms, as they are continually predicting our desires and providing ideas that will provoke and engage us the most. The length of time we remain engaged on the platform, can also be determined by our polarity to the subject. Does the idea feed our fears or celebrate our beliefs? An idea that is predicted to rest in the middle of the spectrum or that won't capture our attention, may be considered by the algorithm as a low priority and not served up for constant viewing. An idea that does not enrage, disgust or perhaps be cherished or celebrated, may be judged unlikely to generate incremental revenue for the platform. The algorithms are not evil, they are, however, increasingly insightful into what triggers human engagement at an individual level. Like the best UFC fighters, we are often primed to come out fighting when we see the opposition in the opposing corner or when we need to play to the crowd. The algorithms know this, and leverage this constantly to keep us entertained.

Arguably, this is potentially becoming a cancerous problem for modern civilisation. One that our ape biology was not necessarily evolved to wrestle with. What ideas will our species select in this provocative, digital environment? Can our own mental algorithms compete with the trillion flops per second of digital algorithmic power? The ones designed to manipulate us for commercial gain by increasing predictive behaviour. After thousands of years of developing faster methods for information exchange, will our most powerful technological ideas be now used against us? Or, Is it already happening?

CHAPTER 6

MISLEADING IDEAS.

During the elections for President Obama in 2008 and 2012, the west was innocently sun-baking in the opinion that social media was becoming a source of pure liberty and unilateral unity. Obama is often regarded as the first "social media President", and undoubtedly used the medium more adeptly than his rivals for communication, community-building, and fund-raising. The year Obama came into office, the White House joined Facebook, Twitter, Flickr, Vimeo, iTunes, and (the now irrelevant) MySpace. In 2013, Michelle Obama posted her first photo to Instagram, and in 2015, President Obama sent his first tweet from @POTUS.[150] Digital media was widely hailed as the "Yes, we can" voice of the people. Communication power had apparently seismically shifted from the elite few, to the popular masses. It was during this period that the "Arab Spring" took root and was heralded as a social-media-led revolution to unseat oppressive regimes across the Middle East. Totalitarian governments were initially technologically behind the curve and were often outflanked by the speed and spread of the various uprisings. They perhaps misjudged the power of the movement, buckled under pressure, and some even toppled. Colonel Gaddafi was arguably the first Dictator in history to have their own death instantly shared to the world from the social media mobile phones of Libyans. He was dragged from a drain, under a road near Sirte, and then beaten and shot in front of the smart-phone enabled mob.[151]

Other significant states around the world began to realise that this new medium may eventually fracture their own power base. Many rapidly deployed systems and tools to help manage these new social platforms and clamp down on dissenting information, and monitor or curtail the power of activists. One of the outcomes of this development has been punishments for using social media in a manner deemed as non-compliant with the defined norms of society. These are now increasingly enforced in many nations against both individuals and the platforms themselves.

The penalty for spreading "fake news" on a social platform in countries like Russia and China can now be up to five years in jail.[152] Amnesty International would likely argue that this is just the tip of the penalty iceberg. Enforcement of social media policies may depend on each nation's subjective definition of what constitutes information as being fake or truthful. Almost by default, the ideas that are more likely to be approved, and then amplified, are those that support, or at best, are not in conflict with a State's existing doctrine and ideology. Deviation from that narrative may be be harshly punished. In a 2020 report, Amnesty International stated that they believed that in markets like Vietnam, the social media platforms "have become hunting grounds for censors, military cyber-troops, and state-sponsored trolls. Amnesty also argues that the platforms themselves are not merely letting it happen, they're increasingly complicit.[153] As partial evidence of this, they stated that, "in April 2020, Facebook announced that it had agreed to "significantly increase" its compliance with requests from the Vietnamese Government to censor "anti-state" posts. It justified this policy shift by claiming the Vietnamese authorities were deliberately slowing traffic to the platform as a warning to the company."

Advances in online data tracking, integrated with real-world facial recognition systems, and other data-sets, means that significant rebellion from this system of idea control seems increasingly unlikely by individuals living in such States if they wish to retain any freedom they have. In China, the number of facial recognition cameras has grown from 176 million in 2017 to an estimated 626 million in 2020.[154] This means that people can be increasingly tracked both online and offline. There is now a limited ability to go "off-the-grid" for citizens of China, as technology is integrated into their daily existence and social compliance systems. Cities like London are not that far behind, with over 640,000 surveillance cameras tracking the actions of 9.3 million people.[155] The justification of this escalation may well be pinned to crime, security, or terrorism, but they may also be used against positive activists and, therefore, the technology may be limiting the spread of potential new ideas as well.

It's not just nations such as China, Turkey, Russia, and Iran who are developing laws to curtail fake ideas being shared on a social platforms. Australia, Canada, France and, Britain have all taken steps in this direction, and the debate between policy-makers in the USA, together with the implications of "de-platforming", is an ongoing issue.[156] This doesn't mean that it is right, or moral, to limit ideas, it just exposes the growing nuances, agendas and debate as to whether an idea is fake, misleading, or disruptive, and more importantly, who controls and defines the definition and its spread.

The liberating digital transparency tools initially wielded by netizens against Dictators in the Arab Spring during 2011, has now been re-engineered and aimed back towards citizens with unrelenting scale, sophistication, and control. There is no escaping the data-tracking abilities of almost any state. The US "whistleblower" Edward Snowden revealed that this was occurring within western democracies, as well as inside Totalitarian states, when he alleged that the US National Security Agency was collecting meta-data on billions of phone-calls made by US citizens.[157] While the "Arab Spring" educated many states on the necessity to have an active digital media management strategy, it is also tipped some of them towards the strategic importance of pro-actively spreading their own social propaganda ideas, as a tool of national offence. Digital ideas can now be borderless, scaleable, anonymous, disguised and an offensive weapon to promote destabilisation, chaos, and regime change. Manipulated social ideas, at the hands of well-funded state actors, can infiltrate a nation faster and with more impact than the best trained, Martini-drinking, secret agent.

One of the leading voices drawing attention to this threat, is the Research Manager at the Stanford Internet Observatory, Renne Di Resta.[158] In 2018, she was asked to testify in front of the US Senate Intelligence Committee, investigating foreign state interference in the 2016 US President Elections. Her testimony to the Committee clearly laid bare the systematic and manipulative approach that was occurring at that time, and has not abated since. She stated, "Propaganda and malign narratives have existed for a very long time, but today's influence operations, which co-opt popular social platforms, are materially different, the propaganda is shared by our friends, often in the form of highly effective, shareable, immediately graspable memes. It is efficiently amplified by algorithms, and the campaigns achieve unprecedented scale." She testified further, "To conduct an operation, adversaries leverage the entire media ecosystem to push a narrative and manufacture the appearance of popular consensus. The operation is planned on one platform, such as a messaging or chat board. Content is created, tested, and hosted on others, such as Reddit, Pinterest, and YouTube. It's then pushed to platforms like Twitter and Facebook, with standing audiences of hundreds of millions of people, and targeted at those most likely to be receptive to it. The platform's trending algorithms are gamed to make the content go viral - this often delivers the added benefit of mainstream media coverage, increasing attention via traditional media channels including television. If an operation is successful and the content gets wide distribution, or if a manipulative page gains enough followers, the recommendation engine and search engine will continue to serve up the content on an ongoing basis."[159]

In summary, nations, advocacy groups, or enemies can leverage the inherent polarising properties of the social media algorithms, to promote the ideas they desire to see advanced in a country and actively amplify selected content with the objective to dramatically fracture opinions. The result can be that impacted communities within the targeted country, may become increasingly tribal and partisan. These actors can deliberately fuel both sides of any debate to promote division and make alignment on a given topic or idea, increasingly harder to achieve within a community or a nation. Moreover, they can create and circulate misleading or false content on all sides of an issue to obscure the truth, raise temperatures, and fester an environment where trust and credibility in discourse, and debates on ideas, may decline in utility.

Most digital media platforms have active programs to delete misleading information and "de-platform" fraudulent users, but the sheer scale and speed of the data exchange means that active management of this issue is incredibly complex. This was documented in the findings of the US Senate Select Committee Inquiry into Russian interference in the 2016 US President Elections which concluded that "Russia's goals were to undermine public faith in the US democratic process."[160] They also noted that social platforms were actively mitigating against misinformation, evidenced by the testimony of Facebook COO, Sheryl Sandberg, with her statement that Facebook's "focus is on inauthenticity, so if something is inauthentic, whether it's trying to influence domestically or trying to influence on a foreign basis and actually, a lot more of the activity is domestic, we take it down."[161] However, the US Senate also concluded that "the current constructs for removing influence operation content from social media are being surpassed by foreign influence operatives, who adapt their tactics to either make their inauthenticity indiscernible, their automated propagation too rapid to control, or their operations compliant with terms of service."[162] In other words, the social media platforms are constantly playing catch-up and plugging the lying leaks in their cracked digital dams.

Ideas targeted to be socially manipulated can cover topics that are vital to the prosperous future of a society, such as political candidates, immigration law, racial equivalence, equal rights, climate change, social welfare, economic policy, and sexism. The dangers of division is certainly not new to the world. In 1858, Abraham Lincoln made a campaign speech at the Illinois Republican State Convention.[163] He had just won the nomination to run for the U.S. Senate. When speaking about the need for society to align on the abolition of slavery, and fearing the prospect of civil war, he famously spoke the words. "a house divided against itself cannot stand." The truth is, that as timely, articulate, inspiring, and important as this speech was, he borrowed the idea from the New Testament Bible which attributes this wisdom to Jesus Christ himself.[164]

Over 2,000 years later, the very idea that communities and countries need to unite upon ideas to build a stronger tomorrow, resonates as pertinent and powerfully as ever. What has radically changed since biblical times, is that our pervasive social media algorithms are often designed and manipulated to optimise and share the content that increases the potential for our houses to be divided. They may never be solely responsible for tearing down institutions and creating total discord, but increasingly, people, states, and other lobbyists are exploring how they take advantage of them, to pour provocative fuel on the burning social bonfires. Society should not be biased or naive enough to believe that it is only "rogue" foreign states pursuing the strategy of division. Their activity, detailed by the US Senate Inquiry, is just evidence that it is increasingly possible to have a sophisticated approach to manipulating social platforms to smear deeply partisan ideas. Domestic politicians, lobby groups, influencers, and anyone with an agenda, can apply similar techniques with debilitating effects given enough resources. In fact, a proportion of the divisive content shown to be amplified in the 2016 US elections was not even generated by foreign states. It was created by pressure groups within America, and then independently amplified by the foreign states. The result of this social activity, is that it may contribute to the increasing polarisation of a nation or, at best, adds to the social clutter so that any better or more balanced ideas are harder to sieve from the slime of the swamp.

This is not just happening within the USA. Since the expansion of social media platforms and the events of the Arab Spring, it is occurring in many nations. Additionally, the confusion and content is not contained to digital platforms. Although the spark may start on social media, the fire then continues to burn throughout real-world experiences. Polarising messages, videos, and information that occur online are often rapidly covered by "opinion pieces" in traditional media and mainstream cable news channels. In turn, they are catalysts for further discussions, debates, protests, and even can provoke physical activation. This then generates a vicious cycle of further online tweets and re-posts. The line between discord on social media and arguments in reality is entangled, and effectively meaningless, because ideas are not restricted by the medium. Ideas, good and bad, true or false, are constantly mobile, contagious, and borderless. Jan Neumann, a former officer with Russia's FSB intelligence service summed it up perfectly in a 2018 interview when he said: "The victims of this war are average people for whom it is almost impossible to figure out who's telling the truth, If you control social media, you win."[165]

Ideas are fundamental and critical to a civilisation's growth, stability, and survival. As a society, we are now inundated with a deluge of potential ideas at a level already exhausting enough for individuals to determine between which are good or bad. This is now being blended with a virtual cocktail of a real-time social spin, manipulation, and amplification. In this flux, people need to ascertain which ideas are true or false, and which are the best for them, their family, and their nation. Is it possible that people can be reliably expected to consistently select the fittest ideas for our prosperity and survival in this convoluted and muddy environment? For the first time in human history, the volume and opaqueness of our ideas may now be far outpacing our biological systems' ability to correctly assess and filter them.

Increasingly, there are important pressure groups that are concerned about this. They include brands, regulators, and policy-makers, but perhaps none more so than the "Center for Humane Technologies" co-founded by its President, Tristan Harris[166]. He has been described as the "closest thing that Silicon Valley has to a conscious". This is simultaneously a credit to him, and a dire assessment as to what might be the "true north" for the rest of the silicon valley juggernaut. The purpose of his organisation is to "Imagine a world built on humane technology that operates for the common good, strengthening our capacity to tackle our biggest global challenges."[167] One interpretation of this mission is that his goal is help build a world where technology assists the selection of good ideas, rather than hindering it.

In 2019, he was asked to share his concerns to the US Senate Sub-Committee for Communications, Technology, Innovation, and the Internet. In his prepared statement, he warned against the escalating effects that digital media algorithms are having on a person's attention and processing capabilities. "How can we solve the world's most urgent problems," he stated "if we've downgraded our attention spans, downgraded our capacity for complexity and nuance, downgraded our shared truth, downgraded our beliefs into conspiracy-theory-thinking that we can't construct shared agendas to solve our problems? This is destroying our sense making at a time we need it the most."[168] While these remarks seemed to be understood and appreciated by the attentive Senators, years following this presentation, no meaningful changes to legislation have emerged. The wheels of Government turn very slowly indeed.

Unfortunately, the COVID19 pandemic exposed the raw fragility of our overly social networked societies. Rancid misinformation, conspiracy theories, and partisan politics often drowned out sensible conversations on good science, good hygiene, good nutrition, and even civic responsibility. It was as if "freedom of speech" had become indivisible with "freedom to lie". In 1918, US Senator Hiram Warren Johnson is purported to have said "The first casualty when war comes, is truth". During the COVID19 pandemic, truth was often collateral damage, if not completely buried, by confusion and lies. Arguably, first in China where the true facts of the dangers were liberated at a speed much too slow to protect World health. One such example, is the appalling case of the Wuhan-based whistleblower, Dr Li Wen Liang, who was among the very first experts to report the existence of a virulent novel disease. He was quickly forced by Chinese police to recant his opinion and compelled to sign a letter stating that he'd made "false comments." Unfortunately, Dr Li died of COVID19 in February 2020 at the young age of 34.[169]

As the virus spread around the world, so did a barrage of conflicting ideas generated by left and right protagonists and amplified to excess by social media. This was then repeated and enhanced by 24 hour cable pundits, influencers, and policy-makers on all sides. It seemed, in many corners of the Earth, that there was more haste and importance given to filling airtime and screens than there was to finding and verifying the facts. If survival of the fittest is now dependent on acting on the very best of humanities ideas, the tragic global death toll from COVID19 showed the devastating impact of a lack of objective knowledge, and the risk to civilisation's global stability from the escalating confusion and polarisation of ideas. The soft underbelly of humanity was exposed by our genetic weakness to grasp true clarity in the face of a hurricane of conflicting, biased, and misleading ideas that surrounded us. If it is now becoming an increasingly difficult task for many people to pluck the best ideas from a virtual storm of options, a mere sixteen years since the launch of social media, where will our society be in fifty years with this rate of exponential idea promotion and growth?

There are multiple scenarios that can halt this debilitating set of affairs from suffocating the future positive progress of our families, cities and nations. The social media platforms could step-up their voluntary self-regulation and aggressively change their algorithm's approach and policies to curtail the problem dramatically. Consumers and brands can also change their media consumption patterns by boycotting these platforms, forcing them to re-invent their content strategies and monetisation systems to attract audiences and revenue in better ways.

The European Union and US regulators could (and undoubtedly will) re-examine the laws that govern the social media industry. For example, Section 230 of the US Communications Decency Act, protects internet platforms from legal liability for the tweets, memes, comments, and videos posted on their sites. Even if these changes were successful, there are 194 other countries on Earth who would all need similar controls to some extent.[170] However, any commitment that a US Politician may have to foster change on this subject, will be equally tempered by the US Constitution's important First Amendment right for free-speech. So, major regulatory change is inherently conflicted with the core values of a functioning democracy.

The self-serving reality is that political communication is one of the biggest benefactors and creators of peddling and promoting dubious content. In fact, a recent Gallop poll ranked US Senators, Congress Members, and Governors in the top 10 most dishonest professions in the USA.[171] Joining them in the race to the bottom-feeders was the flimflam profession of "advertising" often at the core of driving profitability for social media platforms. It appears that those perceived to be engaged in the world's most dishonest professions, are building and monetising the most pervasive media platforms in human history for their equally untruthful counterparts, to both regulate and massively leverage, to win and retain their power. Around 100 years ago, the Pulitzer prize-winning author, Upton Sinclair stated: "It is difficult to get a man to understand something, when his salary depends on his not understanding it."[172] If this insight is true, it may be a while before this ginormous can of a billion social worms is untangled. In the meantime, the problem is likely to naturally escalate, and not improve.

CHAPTER 7

IDEA ORACLES.

In the 8th Century BC, the ancient Greeks were also searching the world for unequivocal truth and direction. Emerging from their soup of confusion, was a trusted source of prophesy know as the Pythia. She was the High Priestess of the Temple of Apollo, her wisdom to predict the future, and ability to influence decisions, was legendary across the ancient world. We know her today as the "Oracle of Delphi", who's role was to convey to humanity the true wisdom of Apollo, the God of Prophecy.[173] The exalted position of the Priestess was continually consulted by Kings, Queens, and sages for a period of over 1,000 years, up until the 4th Century AD. If you needed guidance on a nascent idea, such as a fresh war, conquest, investment, or marriage, and truly needed an insightful answer, the Oracle of Delphi was the closest thing ancient Greece had to Siri for over a millennium.

This longevity is outstanding in a modern technology context. Today, new software is updated on a hyper-frequent basis. Software even ten years old is often no longer compatible with new hardware. However, the Greeks had a trusted and valuable insight-generating system that had no new updates, infrastructure, or operating system for over 1,000 years. There are over 500 supposed statements attributable to the Oracle, that have survived through the ages as either anecdotes or proverbs. One such story is from 67 AD, when the Roman Emperor Nero, visited the Priestess for a splash of some much-needed wisdom. She predicted that "The number 73" would mark the hour of his downfall. Nero assumed that this implied he would continue to rule for another forty-two prosperous years, until he reached the ripe age of seventy-three years old. Instead, only a year later in AD 68, he was executed by his own guard in his palace. The General, Galba, was then proclaimed the new Emperor of Rome by the Senate. Emperor Galba was coincidently seventy-three at the time.[174] With an ironic wink to the ancient deities of forecasting, Google Maps now provides guided directions to the ruined and abandoned temple of the Oracle of Delphi. It is roughly a 181 km, two hour drive north/west of modern day Athens, along the E75.

The demise of the legendary Oracle of Delphi was due to the rise of a new idea across the Mediterranean world, Christianity. The Greek Gods' power and influence was slipping though their immortal fingers and, therefore, Apollo's perceived ability to guide the future was declining in both esteem and real-world value. In early 394 AD, the powerful Byzantine Emperor, Theodosius, outlawed the pagan practices of these ancient Greek religions, putting an end to the power of the Oracle of Delphi, forever.[175] Although the birth of Christ had occurred 300 years earlier, the mighty Apollo didn't see his decline of divine rule coming, and failed to warn his very own Oracle of this event. Clearly an oversight on his part, as Apollo's once venerable status has now sunk to, among other things, being a brand of budget toothpaste in India, and the 14th largest tyre company in the world[176], however, he is no longer the principle God of choice for the planet.

Whether the Oracle gathered her insight from magic potions, shamanic rituals, divine interface with the true Apollo, or a flip of a drachma, is not exactly known or perhaps even relevant. What is more pertinent, is when deciding which idea to follow, when faced with a crossroad, humans have held a long-standing tradition of delegating decisions to divine Oracles of all shapes and sizes. While some Gods through our long history may have not been infallible, others have remained steadfast and continually worshipped. Millions of people continue to put their directional faith in their God, passionately and earnestly asking them to guide their decisions. Gods other than Apollo of course, although some reports suggest that as many as 100,000 people are still praying to these ancient Greek Gods.[177]

However uplifting, honest, purposeful, or pure each individual's faith is in their God, there is still no universal human alignment as to whether there is a singular God to ask for guidance with idea selection, as there are still many different religions around the world. After 7,000 years of human civilisation, it currently still comes down to personal faith. For example, there are over a billion people who currently worship the Hindu religion which has three main gods with their three female counterparts. In Japan, millions of people identify with the Shinto religion, which has over eight million different spirits and Gods that can be called upon for different purposes and guidance. These spirits can be connected to a sacred place, or take an animal form to provide timely messages or warnings.

If someone is unsure as to which deity they should request assistance from, then the planet already has a great deal of options available, as there are over 4,000 active religions available on the holy menu. This is not to denigrate one religion over another, or conclude that God doesn't exist. Far from it. Religion plays an important part in moral codes, social cohesion, and can fuel conviction, purpose and, strength in millions of people on a daily basis. Religion, as an idea, is often a critical and defining part of a person, a community, and sometimes a nation. The unbroken chain of historical diversity of religious ideas and groups simply illustrates that a universal human agreement on a single religious idea has not been achieved since the dawn of society. This is despite the countless prayers, sermons, sacrifices, miracles, debates, inquisitions, burnings, crusades, and wars aimed at settling the subject once and for all.

In 1956, US President Dwight D. Eisenhower signed into law "In God We Trust" to become his nation's official motto, although it had been consistently stamped on US coins since 1864.[178] It has subsequently been printed on every piece of US currency, adorned in classrooms, and the Florida car licence plate also enshrines it as an option. Eisenhower wanted the motto to be a galvanising spiritual weapon and a renewable resource in the fight against another idea, communism, which was then propagating the policy of state atheism.[179] The momentum for it to become the nation's motto, began innocently in 1814 when Francis Scott Key wrote the epic phrase, in his heroic poem "Defence of Fort M'Henry". These words were later to be set to music, and would eventually become the official US National Anthem, "The Star Spangled Banner" in 1931.[180]

The selection of the motto was a strategic counter-strike in the Cold War against the USSR. It did not conflict with the US Constitution, which forbids linking church and state, in that the motto did not define which particular God a person should trust in. Indeed, the phrase itself can be originally found in both the Old Testament and the Quran.[181] This motto, therefore, elegantly reflects that the world, and the US in-particular, is a melting pot of many established religions including Catholics, Protestants, Buddhists, Muslims, Judaism, and other important groups. While religion can a be purposeful and a beautiful component of life, the reality is that the USA, let alone all of humanity, cannot rapidly align on delegating the selection of an important idea to any one particular deity, if it was ever urgently required. It is, and will always remain, based on the individual, no matter what slogan is printed on the mighty dollar bill. People who are already religious, have found their true choice of God, to help guide their selection of ideas and navigate complexity and truth in life.

However, because there are multiple religions, when it comes to delegating the assessment of an idea to a single religion and potentially receiving a unified response across the planet, seems highly unlikely to succeed. Any divine instructions, if received, would naturally depend upon which religion the idea is presented to for consideration and guidance. There are also approximately 21% of Americans who claim no religious identity and, presumably, don't ask for direction from anyone above.[182] To rely on religion as a true-north for idea selection, for the future of humanity, is at best, a subjective path and not a universally objective one.

Human history has also been littered with a multitude of eclectic, much less purposeful, and incredibly dubious ways to delegate responsibility for the selection of ideas. The society that had the first bad idea, in the random field of divination, may be lost in time, but the Sumerians in the 2nd Millennium BC would surely have been keen to stake a claim. They were committed to studying the disembowelled entrails of sacrificed sheep to yield truth. This was so important to them that they conveniently left behind beautifully detailed clay models of sheep livers for present-day historians to marvel at.[183] The delicate contours of these ancient livers are mapped and preserved in exquisite detail. Expert Priests, known as the Baru, would be called upon to read the terrain of the freshly butchered sheep organs to determine the choices that their Kings should make in all manners of important decisions. This practice of idea selection is even referenced in the Old Testament, in Ezekiel 21:21.[184] When faced with a decision to attack the ancient cities of Rabbah or Judah, the King Of Babylon consulted a liver for clarity and wisdom. Apparently, the city of Judah in modern-day Palestine, received the liver's vote for "idea of the month" and the King decisively invaded it in 597 BC and emphatically won. This practice, know as Haruspicy,[185] must have somehow consistently provided a perceived degree of valuable data, as it was used continuously throughout the ages. Even the Roman Empire was still consulting entrails as a decision tool well into 400 AD.

Humanity kicked this idea up a notch with the horrific practice of Anthropomancy.[186] This is the same idea as the Sumerians' hatched, but now using the entrails of women and children instead of a sheep. This is cruelty way beyond the historically, much more common practice of human sacrifice, which hoped to appease the Gods with a brutal death to gain favour for a more productive outcome. Anthropomancy was often the study of entrails at the moment of death itself. Predictions were made based upon death throes, number and volume of screams, direction of blood flow, or various other macabre interpretations of the sadistic event. This practice is first documented in Ancient Egypt, but perhaps the most infamous alleged practitioners were the Roman Emperors, Elagabalus (218 to 222 AD) and Julian the Apostate (361 to 363 AD). They have both been linked to child sacrifice to better-shape their decisions.[187] These rulers were, broadly speaking, unspeakably depraved even on the very best days.

There have been hundreds of other wild ideas that humans have leaned upon for the guidance of important idea selection. The flights of birds, the movement of mice, the roll of rings, the melting of metal, the flicker of a fire, the turn of a taro, the bounce of a bone, the humps on a head, and the push of dung by a dung beetle have all been in favour at various historical times to help people decide whether to stay or go, fight or flee, marry or divorce.[188]

Some divination practices are still legitimately and widely practiced today. In Buddhist and Taoist temples throughout Asia, the Kau Cim practice of shaking one hundred bamboo sticks out of a cup is still used on a daily basis by millions of people to reveal mystical answers to prayers after 2,000 years of successful tradition.[189] In Japan, some temples provide fortunes called "omikuji". If the individual feels that the fortune they've drawn is unwanted or negative, they can simply tie it at a special area called "musubidokoro", and that fortune will then be reversed.[190] While in Bolivia, it is not unheard of for people to consult a "Yatiri". They are gifted and respected people who can forecast the future by reading the leaves of the local coca plant.[191]

If you assume that western civilisations have established a more analytical system for selecting ideas, and not swayed by such superstitions, you would be mistaken. Research suggests that around 25% of western civilisation currently believes in Astrology, and regularly reviews their daily horoscope to help shuck pearls of wisdom.[192] Horoscopes are commonplace in many major publications, and there are famous Astrologers, such as The Astro Twins, Debbie Frank, and Chain Nicholas who read Horoscopes to the both the enthralled masses and superstars such as Beyonce.[193]

Although the first evidence of the Zodiac is 4,000 years old,[194] the practice of connecting our fate to the movement of the constellations and the planets is still gaining traction. The millennial generation are increasingly looking for astrological direction amongst a sea of social media stars.[195] Incredibly, these often factually-impotent horoscopes may actively influence and shape millions of daily decisions. Studies have shown that people may instinctively rally against a given negative personal horoscope. If the Zodiac prediction suggests that a bad day is looming, then people will often respond by selecting an indulgent idea to help improve their chances of a better day.[196] Humans instinctively rebel against the notion of a defined fate, like the fabled King Canute, commanding the tides to reverse direction in his presence. Whether deliberately, or subconsciously, people in every corner of the planet are constantly rolling the dice of chance, using superstitions to guide choices or select ideas, just as they have always done for thousands of years.

When it comes to many of life's important and daily decisions we sometimes use our intellect, combined with superstitions, to find a path forward in life. The cognitive dissonance is that despite humanity's pool of rapidly advancing knowledge, combined with the most powerful and instantaneous information tools in history, our species is still often inclined to let the proverbial dung beetle "take the wheel" when it comes to idea selection. We, therefore, place a proportion of our future success in the equivalent hands of an ouija board. In October 2020, a few weeks before the US Presidential Elections, Astrologer and Cosmic Alchemist, Adama Sesey was asked for predictions on what was about to unfold. Her view was, "Mercury rules written and verbal communication and information. When it's retrograde, we can experience misinformation, disorganisation, and unexpected truths being revealed. All of this can cause some confusion and inaccuracy in the voting process. Fast-forward to astrology in December, Jupiter and Saturn will join in the radical sign of Aquarius. This will trigger the collective to rise up and seek to change what is no longer working in governments on a global scale."[197] On January 6th 2021, protestors stormed the US Capitol. Was the idea to rebel and riot propelled by the stars, as seemingly predicted by the Astrologer, or simply influenced by the President or a chat board? Our mental algorithms are designed to judge the potential of an idea, and will be, almost by definition, hit and miss. As a race, we sometimes exhibit qualities more closely associated with a troop of puppets when it comes to following ideas. Especially when a perceived oracle or authority pulls the strings and gives us motivation or convincing direction. We often blindly follow their instructions to either glorious victory or embarrassing defeat.

This has also been echoed throughout history in all the documented dubious medical treatments we collectively decided were good ideas to ingest, to our determinant. The term "snake-oil" salesman, blankets an extensive range of ideas that have promised health and delivered either nothing, or at worse, death. It originates from the mid-19th century, when over 180,000 Chinese labourers landed in America to help create the expansion of the transcontinental railway network.[198] They carried with them a traditional medical oil made from the Chinese Water Snake. This was naturally rich in fatty acids like Omega-3, which has anti-inflammatory properties useful as topical relief for symptoms of arthritis and joint pain. However, an entrepreneurial salesman, Clark Stanley, turned to the much more accessible, native Rattle Snake, to produce and market his own brand of medicated oil.[199] He launched it with both hype and applause at the 1893 World's Columbian Exposition in Chicago, where he sliced and boiled a live snake on stage and scooped out the rising fat to illustrate the wonder and purity of his innovation. His demonstration clearly worked. His business expanded, and he established two manufacturing sites in Massachusetts and Rhode Island.

Unfortunately for Mr Stanley and his customers, this particular species of snake had almost 70% less Omega-3 then it's Chinese relative, and thus, the oil was nowhere near as beneficial. As bad as this fact was, it was still not the main problem. In 1917, US Federal Investigators seized and tested shipments of his Snake Oil Liniment, and declared that there was not a fang-drop of genuine snake oil in the recipe. Instead, it contained a mineral oil, believed to be beef fat, combined with red pepper and turpentine. The result was that it was deemed as a particularly pointless product. He was fined $20, and the term "Snake Oil Salesman" was forever bitten into our culture as a lexicon for concocting a false medical idea.

Either by deliberate design, or through ignorance, we have had a long and retrospectively embarrassing history of attempting to keep our species alive based on ideas with very little merit. The ancient Greek Fathers of Medicine propagated their share of bad medical ideas. One example, is their assertion that schizophrenia, panic attacks, and other mental disorders in women, are caused by the physical movement of their uterus. This was given the name "wandering womb" and is attributed to the ancient Greek and Roman physicians, such as Hippocrates (460 - 370 BC) and Areteaus (2nd century BC). Their idea was to classify the womb as a separate "animal entity" operating within the female body. It could move independently inside the body, and when it did, it would result in identifiable psychological aliments. If the womb crept upwards, then this resulted in a lack of strength, energy, or perhaps vertigo. A downwards dash of the womb would be revealed by women choking, loosing the ability to speak, or even death.[200] These wise Greek men also then had very rock-solid ideas on how to resolve these conditions, by cleverly tempting the womb back into place. Recommended prescriptions used special concoctions encased in vaginal suppositories, that either attracted or repelled the belligerent womb to wander back into its rightful position. Additionally, these predictably male Greek physicians, also recommend keeping the womb distracted and occupied, via the treatment of constant sex, and ultimately pregnancy for the most troublesome of womb cases.

The remnants of this illogical idea survived in our civilisation for almost 1,500 years, as uterus aromatherapy was still widely used for female psychological aliments in Europe until the 15th Century.[201] It, perhaps, could be excused and explained that science simply didn't have the facts for over a millennium to acquire a better understanding or idea. However, it should have been painfully obvious during the entire time, that many men had exactly the same psychological conditions, without the interjection of a roaming uterus. However, despite the same symptoms in men, doctors weren't recommending to inject a mixture of goat's dung and rose oil into male genitals to tempt their testicles back into position, as they frequently prescribed for their female patient's pesky womb.

The history of bad medical idea selection did eventually strike a gender balance. When it came to the ancient problem of erectile disfunction, male doctors created equally disjointed ideas to reverse the softness in their groins. Many of these required eating a testosterone-rich testicle, or two. A UK-based Urologist, Jyoti Shah, has written extensively on the global spread of this approach known as organotherapy.[202] The ancient Indian Sanskrit texts, the Sushruta Samhita, date back to the 8th Century BC, and includes the earliest remedies that men eagerly followed to solve their erectile problems. The first documented idea involved the rather pedestrian consumption of goat testes boiled in milk. For more impact, a lotion of clarified butter, boiled together with the testes of alligators, mice, frogs and sparrows was to be rubbed into the soles of the feet. Later, the Roman's idea was to consume the penis of particularly virile animals like a rabbit or a tiger. If the animal was overly horny, then simply eat their horny parts. In some cases, this idea was extended to a mixed cocktail of a soaring Eagle's excrement, blended with a dash of a firm young man's frothy semen, to enable the little Emperor to conquer again. Undoubtedly, over the centuries, countless legions of desperate men have followed these ideas to the letter. They ate, drank, and rubbed all sorts of snake-oil concoctions to improve their sexual performance, mostly in vain. These are, of course, ancient medicinal ideas, largely debunked by modern science. Yet, over time these types of ideas have slowly morphed from the secret wisdom of authorities, into deeply cemented cultural beliefs, which continue to be both believed, and defended across generations.

In the early 1920s, American businessman, and self-proclaimed "surgeon", John R. Brinkley, convinced hundreds of men that the surgical implantation of goat testicles into their abdomen would cure their impotence, as well as many other aliments. Thankfully, he was eventually widely discredited, and bankrupt by 1941, but not before he successfully opened "Goat Gland Clinics" in several American States. These venues were rudimentarily skilled at implanting testicles into hundreds of people from across the country. In his twenty-year-long business, he was known for causing a number of deaths, supporting Nazis, and at one point, sponsoring a Kansas baseball team to promote his business, The Brinkley Goats.[203] He even created his own radio station near the Mexican border so that his dangerous ideas on organotherapy could be broadcast to the desperate, far and wide.

Many people would confidently say that these ideas were only accepted by our ignorant ancestors, who may have based their decisions on much less science and knowledge than we have access to today. If that was the case, surely our society would not make the same mistakes today? However, people are still seeking similar remedies and will often accept absurd ideas despite no scientific evidence to support their efficacy. Throughout the world, and especially in Asian markets like China and Vietnam, tiger and bear penis is still widely believed to provide erectile power, nearly 3,000 years since the first recording of these ideas. Tiger penis soup is currently an idea that numerous Beijing businessmen will pay as much US$5,700 per bowl to enjoy.[204] Despite the fact that the trade in Tiger parts is now internationally banned, it is still prospering and growing. Apparently, it has been easier for humans to kill tigers by the millions, than to drive the ancient idea of organotherapy to extinction.

Our ability to listen to Oracles, leaders, social influencers and other people with medicinal "bad ideas", yet process them positively through our mental algorithms, is an ongoing and conflicted process that often results in community peril. This was again demonstrated during the beginning of the COVID19 pandemic. Various global political and medical leaders erroneously promoted unfounded ideas on the benefits of ingesting substances like disinfectants to cure the virus. Most medical experts immediately chastised these ideas, but many citizens readily accepted them as gospel. Following the public statements by powerful politicians in favour of bleach ingestion, the American Association of Poison Control Center reported a highly significant increase in people ingesting disinfectants. In January, February, and March of 2020, accidental poisonings in the USA from household disinfectants were up respectively by 5%, 17%, and 93% over the same months in 2019. In April 2020, following US Presidential statements supporting potential benefits from disinfectants, the increase jumped to 121% compared to the previous year. In early May 2020, poisonings were still up by 69% over the same period in 2019.[205]

Another of the then-US President's "no harm in trying" ideas was his persistent tweets in favour of the anti-malaria compound, Hydroxychloroquine, first approved for medicinal use in the USA in 1955. This drug was touted by various political and opinion leaders as both a cure, and a preventative medicine for COVID19. Even the US President proudly indicated that he was taking it himself.[206] Many medical experts, such as the US FDA, feverishly objected that there was no scientific basis for this idea, and warned that there was emerging evidence that for those patients with pre-existing heart complications, it may increase the risk from the virus.[207] Despite the cavernous gap in clinical and independent positive evidence for the efficacy of Hydroxychloroquine, demand for the drug surged during the second quarter of 2020. Sales doubled to US$50 million, and prescriptions surged to 830,000 from only 460,000 in 2019.[208] It seems highly unlikely that seeking protection from malaria laden mosquitos, while traveling through Sub-Sahara Africa, was driving the rise in US demand during this period. Clearly, thousands of people actively followed the ideas broadcast by their President and other influencers. Perhaps they would have also inserted John R. Brinkley's goats testicles as a cure, if tweeted to do so.

This ancient path of following "snake-oil" ideas was not only limited to people following their leaders in the USA. On the other side of the world in Iran, over 700 people died from the ingestion of methanol in an attempt to cure the COVID19 virus.[209] Partly due to confusion as the government had urgently allowed for an official increase in ethanol production, but only for external use in hand sanitisers. Unfortunately, a large number of people were misled into believing that instead of disinfecting their hands with it, they would be better advised to treat it like a cough syrup and drink enough to poison themselves.

In Belarus, their unique President recommended ice-hockey, vodka, and the sauna as a cure for COVID19.[210] At least there were no apparent accidental deaths as a result of this. As Belarus is already the world's fifth largest vodka market,[211] they were perfectly placed, and presumably eager, to capitalise on this claimed cure. On the Indian subcontinent, a politician from the BJP party in the Northern State of Assam, had less appetising ideas on how to beat the global pandemic. Her view was that an elixir of scared cow dung and urine, called "gaumutra", should be ingested to purify the body and kill the virus.[212] The President of another Indian political organisation, the Akhil Bharat Hindu Mahasabh (ABHM) Party, went one step further and organised "gaumutra" parties, where enthusiastic people lined up in street markets, to take a shot of this divine fluid, convinced it would prevent the dreaded virus.[213] The leader of the ABHM Party stated to his followers that COVID19 was an "avatar" that had "come to punish those who eat non-vegetarian food". In the defence of the ABHM Party, gaumutra has been used for centuries in parts of India to help combat other illnesses such as leprosy, fever, ulcers, liver, and kidney disorders. While there is little evidence of medical success for these ailments, it has been scientifically shown to have potential anti-microbial benefits[214], but this is still a large leap of logic as a COVID19 cure. By April 2021, India was fully engulfed in the raging pandemic with millions suffering and hundreds of thousands dead.

Finally, in Mexico, the Governor of the State of Puebla, home to 1.25 million people, publicly declared his belief that COVID19 only targeted the most affluent people, and therefore the poor citizens that inhabited his state, which had presumably voted him into office, would be immune and protected.[215] His naive insight was driven by his own astute observations that the earliest cases of the virus were only found in people rich enough to afford travel. As a result, he presumably assumed it was their wealth that was the cause, and not their interaction with the virus in other locations. Tragically, by mid 2021, Puebla was one of the hardest-hit States in Mexico with over 11,000 deaths.

How many lives could have been saved, illnesses prevented, or businesses protected with the rapid acceptance and clearer communication of better medical ideas, preventative measures, or just less conflicting ideas, may never truly be known. The problem is not only that there were bad medical ideas, promoted by the people empowered by society, but additionally that these ideas were then massively multiplied across mainstream and social media. It's equally problematic that in the minds of millions of people, their bespoke mental algorithms selected these snake-oil remedies as the best of all possible ideas that were being offered, and then duly acted upon them. This was despite other health and nutritional information being equally accessible, but perhaps not amplified in their social feeds or TV screens. Just like our fellow ancient Greeks 2,000 years earlier, our civilisation was curiously compelled to follow false narratives that, on many levels, paralleled the insanity of an idea such as "wandering wombs".

Urban culture might cheekily refer to these repetitive occurrences as a continuing example of "survival of the fittest" or the "Darwin Awards", where the dumbest of our species spectacularly, and sometimes thankfully, remove themselves from the gene pool. However, this continuing selection of bad ideas may not exactly be a hardware issue driven by our genes. Its relentless persistence throughout human history may indicate that it is more of a "software issue", of how our mental algorithms continually make mistakes in the absorption and processing of information and ideas. It seems that our mental algorithms, no matter the historic period or narrative, has often showcased our limitations in sorting the proverbial bull from the turd when following the ideas promoted by all manners of Oracles. We now live in period where there is terabytes of more information than civilisation has ever previously encountered. To be useful, this data ultimately needs to be assessed, not just by digital algorithms, but by our mental software, operating on genetic hardware that has not significantly changed in 300,000 thousand years. Additionally, any prospective idea, whether it's good, bad, or ugly can be now be globalised and escalated to billions of people in a blink of a pixel. A bad or a good idea is no longer a local problem, it can be instantaneously everywhere and impacting everyone.

The panic-buying of toilet paper in the early days of COVID19 is a prime, albeit ludicrous, example of our species' heard mentality when it comes to ideas. Objectively, it clearly made no sense, but subjectively, millions of people around the world were suddenly prepared to irrationally hoard, steal, stab, brawl, and be tasered for a ply of these sublimely soft squares.[216] Leading psychologist, pundits, and game theorists have sought to explain this mass panic, but the simple matter is that these people thought it was a good idea at the time to hoard toilet paper (if they even though about it all). While many individuals may consistently make the right choices when presented with a basket of potential ideas, to assume that, as a species, we will be collectively highly-skilled at plucking the prized ideas from the exploding exponential volume of digitally catapulted misinformation, is optimistic at best and it is not always backed by the anecdotal evidence.

We often collectively act with the mental agility of lemmings, and enthusiastically follow the next tweeting politician, leader, celebrity, astrologer, or the appropriately termed, "digital-influencer" straight off the nearest cliff. Not dissimilar to our ancient cousins, desperately hanging on the prophetic words of the Oracle of Delphi. The difference is that back then, there was only one appointed Oracle offering advice on ideas, now there are literally millions of them on Instagram to follow.

CHAPTER 8

THE IDEA ECONOMY.

Society and all of humanity naturally lives and loves on a statistical bell-curve. There is bound to be a randomised distribution of people who's experiences and mental algorithms, make them absolutely appalling at selecting good ideas in their everyday lives. Then, the bulk of humanity will marry, work, and play comfortably in the hearty and healthy meat of the curve, consistently making a mix of good, bad, and the odd ugly idea selection. Then, there will be the rare, exalted few that seem to have the consistent ability to divine brilliant ideas, magically plucked from the cloud, fabricated by their bold conviction and unparalleled intellect, or just by sheer willpower. The dynamics of the free-market economy generally ensures that these individuals are generously rewarded and applauded for their unique abilities.

The ideas that they summon into existence are sought after and prioritised by the market for capital investment, progression, and then distribution to the masses for consumption and hopefully, life improvement, in ways great and small. These talented people often become leading entrepreneurs who create everything from new categories, to new industries, and new ways of life. In the process, they also collect millions, if not, billions, in net-worth as compensation for their skill, insight, ideas, and legacy.

In an increasingly materialistic world, our society glues its attention to entrepreneurs who have impressively demonstrated the consistent ability to select ideas that have disrupted history and impacted the world. They possess the modern-day equivalent of turning water into wine, while simultaneously feeding society with their IPO's, product launches, and their GDP-sized alimony payments. Our society, and especially the media, is compelled to seek out their wisdom, while world markets dance to their click-bait sound bites, as if they were issuing new commandments, chiselled into silicon stone.

Accordingly, our society increasingly, and perhaps passively, delegates some of our most important idea selections to these successful entrepreneurs. The dynamic market economy that emerged, following both the industrial revolution and the growth of multinational company structures, has increased access to capital markets and powered investment in exponential technological growth. Over the last one hundred years, there has been a continuous parade of entrepreneurial oracles that have been economically worshipped for their ideas. Edison, Bell, Westinghouse, Hughes, Rockefeller, Arden, Ellison, Chanel, Gates, Stewart, Jobs, Bezos, Dell, Winfrey, Musk, Zuckerberg, Schulz to name just a worthy few.

Legendary automotive innovator and leader, Henry Ford is often quoted as saying "If I had asked people what they wanted, they would have said, faster horses!" Whether he truly said those words may be lost to history, but he was reportedly skeptical of his saddled customers' ability to share his vision for the motorised future, or even conceptualise the impending combustion-powered revolution.[217] The implication is that the average person couldn't judge a good idea even if it was about to run them over. At the time, Henry Ford may have been justified to feel that he needed to create his own path. Mainstream voices during the late 1890s, backed up the notion that Ford was rushing down the wrong investment road. In 1899, the then influential publication, Literary Digest, stated that, "The horseless carriage is at present a luxury for the wealthy and although its price will probably fall, it will never come into as common use as the bicycle".[218] In that year, America had only a total of 4,000 automobiles and 10 million bikes creaking along the dusty streets. Clearly, many people only perceived the horseless-carriage as an idea designed for the elite, and not fulfilling Henry Ford's vision as a transportation tool for the masses.

In spite of these negative predictions, the idea of the car and the automotive industry grew dramatically, and by 1903, the first transcontinental US trip for a gas-powered vehicle occurred, when a slightly used, two-cylinder 20 bhp Winton, traveled from San Francisco to New York in 63 speedy days.[219] It was completed by a young American physician, Horatio Jackson. The feat was astonishing, not only because he had no previous driving experience, or the fact that there were essentially no paved roads across America, but because, he had the idea only five days before embarking on the trip. It was a fifty dollar bet, instigated over a dinner, which started the bumpy adventure. This drive was the beginning of a revolutionary new form of freedom and transport. Today, there are now over 6.5 million km of roads weaving throughout America, and over thirty cars are sold every single second in the USA alone.[220]

In the same year that Horatio triumphantly arrived in New York, Henry Ford's lawyer, Horace Rackham, was being courted to invest in his client's fledgling automotive company. He was unsure of the idea, and sought the opinion, on Ford's business potential, from the President of the Michigan Savings Bank. He infamously advised Rackham, "The horse is here to stay, but the automobile is only a novelty." Luckily for Horace Rackham, he ignored that erroneous wisdom and proceeded to invest US$5,000 for 100 shares in Ford. Nine years later in 1912, the shares that he held were bought back by Edsel Ford for US$12.5 million.[221] Rackham's reward for backing the idea, was that he was able to spend the rest of his life as a philanthropist, giving money to children's charities and other worthy causes.

Ford was proven to be insightful, he possessed the ability to judge an idea as being good. At least, this first big idea, and perhaps only for a limited time. Many consumers eventually disagreed with the Ford monotonous approach to ordering a standardised specification. In the 1920s, General Motors started responding to consumers' ideas and personalised the design of their cars for emerging needs and segments. Ford continued their resolute focus on assembly line consistency.[222] At the start of the 1920s, Ford sold 66% of their cars in the US. By the time the company needed to retool and respond to consumer needs, beginning with the Model A in 1927, that figure had dropped to a low of 15%. Ford, like every genius entrepreneur, was not infallible. They can be the first to spot a great idea and then, soon after, completely miss the next big one as well.

Breakthrough ideas are not easy to consistently catch. Leading entrepreneurs are continually and automatically punished by market forces and burning stock prices for any failure of their own mental algorithms to guarantee the successful outcome of their innovations. However, it could be argued that the profitability of customer segmentation in the automotive industry was not the greater and much more important idea that Ford, and practically the entire automotive industry, seemingly missed at that time.

In 1900, of the 4,192 cars produced in the United States, just 936 of them ran on gasoline, 1,681 ran on steam, and 1,575 were electric.[223] Incredibly, almost 78% of all the cars manufactured in that year, therefore, ran on zero carbon emissions. Regrettably, by 1914, the actions of American car buyers had put that statistic in full reverse. Ninety-nine percent of the 568,000 automobiles produced in America in 1914 now relied on the internal combustion engine, powered by carbon emitting gasoline. Burning oil was now the "good idea" that people almost unanimously selected, and this regrettably parked clean energy in the automotive sector for decades to come. Longer trips on better roads, poor battery power, and cheaper oil drove consumers away from electric cars. The industry rapidly followed in their wake to take advantage of the rising demand and flowing profits. The industrial decision to focus on oil was part of a giant leap that would set the world down a destructive road of releasing historic levels of carbon from fossil fuels. This eventually helped to create issues like "Petrostates", resource wars, altering geo-politics, and ultimately, contributing to the looming planet-wide catastrophe of climate change. In 1914, combustion must have seemed like a good idea, because our planet may be incredibly different today if the other choices had been selected for development.

The long-term consequences of pumping fossil fuels instead of cleaner energy, were presumably not factored into the decisions that turned the wheels of the fledgling automotive industry in this dramatically different direction. The key parameters of sustainability simply weren't entered into the mental algorithms of either the manufactures or consumers. The market economy, worked as it always does, without a conscious. Driven only by the frictionless immediacy of meeting supply with demand. Its mechanisms often select the ideas that are popular, accessible, and most profitable. This doesn't automatically equate to the "best ideas", as transparency on all essential parameters are not always included in the market dynamics. The invisible hand of the market-economy didn't calculate the weight of the potential long-term negatives from the extrapolated impact on both humanity and the environment, from an idea like the combustion of fossil fuels. Arguably, nor did leaders like Henry Ford, his fellow automotive pioneers, and their investors include these long-term climate consequences in their own share-holder and corporate considerations.

The industry's goal was primarily to capitalise on the rapid expansion of market share and deliver a return on investment to their brave financial backers. Electric cars were widely recognised at the time as being quieter, easier to drive, and less polluting but the investment required to solve the technological challenges of range extension did not seem to be an attractive idea.[224] A more appealing option may have been to leave those problems for future generations of engineers to crash into. Perhaps there was an excuse for the industry, in that they simply didn't have the carbon impact knowledge one hundred years ago, to make this kind of assessment. If so, the industry could not possibly be held morally accountable for their idea selection. Unfortunately, that is not entirely the case.

In 1896, the Swedish scientist Svante Arrhenius, was the first to claim, with empirical data, that fossil fuel combustion may eventually result in enhanced global warming.[225] Importantly, he was not an obscure scientist by any measure. He was directly involved in originating both the Nobel Institute and the Nobel Prize, and was himself awarded a Nobel Prize for Chemistry in 1903. In 1912, he was prestigiously appointed to be a Foreign Honorary Member of the American Academy of Arts and Sciences.

On both sides of the Atlantic, he was an important voice in science, and was raising awareness on the dangers to humanity from releasing massive amounts of carbon into the atmosphere. Based on extensive research and calculations, he proposed an exponential relationship between atmospheric carbon dioxide concentrations, and increasing temperatures. His research linked these higher concentrations to geological periods of low temperatures, resulting in ice-ages and global warming. In 1908, he accurately predicted that the impact of human activity on the climate would limit the potential for new ice-ages when he stated, "Warm ages have alternated with glacial periods, even after man appeared on the earth, we have to ask ourselves: Is it probable that we shall, in the coming geological ages, be visited by a new ice period that will drive us from our temperate countries into the hotter climates of Africa? There does not appear to be much ground for such an apprehension. The enormous combustion of coal by our industrial establishments suffices to increase the percentage of carbon dioxide in the air to a perceptible degree." [226]

Svante Arrhenius was an early and important visionary on climate change. He was Al Gore, a century before Al Gore, was Al Gore. If only he was broadcasting his message via social media, combined with an evocative multi-media slide-show, as apposed to a quill pen, then the planet may be in a very different place today. The frustrating fact is that, as a species, we had accesses to some of the science on climate change, and we knew the potential problems from burning fossil fuels. It just didn't rank very high in our species' collective mental algorithms, when compared to convenience, profits, and expansion of oil. There was more money to be made from the exploitation of short-term ideas rather than a long-term, species-level commitment to a better and more sustainable idea, already in consumer hands, and leading the market. This ideas was zero emission cars.

Despite the massive global attention, the avalanche of science, climate disasters, and now the accessible automotive innovation from leaders like Tesla, Toyota, and other brands, our species is still embracing the objectively better idea of "lower carbon emissions" with the all enthusiasm of an overweight arthritic snail with time to kill. In 1900, 37% of all US car sales were fully electric, yet as we entered 2020 they were woefully under 2%.[227] Apparently, good ideas are as complex for humans to accept today as they were one hundred years ago. The idea that market forces will guide society to the optimal long-term decision is either erroneous, or, at best, the arc of the market is so long that a great deal of collateral damage can be inflicted during the journey. The consequences from pursuing a lesser idea may not just be for the individual, but it can be for the community, or to the planet, and, therefore, our species. The scale of the idea, the ability for it to be borderless, and the quicker it can be deployed, the greater the implied risk of getting it wrong.

Today, with the immense speed and power of our technological ideas tantalisingly at our disposal, we can no longer simply afford a few decades of bad idea selection, let alone hundreds of years before we change direction and attempt to set matters right. The risk to our future is far too great. History may have been more forgiving a thousand years ago when technological change was slower, our capabilities were much less advanced, communities were more isolated, and the population of the Earth was a tenth of what it is today. Now that this has irrevocably changed, the consequences from bad idea selection has dramatically escalated. We now possess the speed, the tools, and the scale to ensure that a truly bad idea can have a devastating global impact in a faster time period, then ever before in all of human history.

The reality, is that even for the smartest entrepreneur, launching a great idea one day and then completely missing the next, is not limited to bonafide visionaries like Henry Ford. It is not only systemic across the entire idea sector, but many leading entrepreneurs argue that failure is an essential part of increasing the probability of future success. Failure creates experiences, which sharpens and strengthens mental algorithms, and improves the chances of future success in selecting subsequent ideas. Celebrated entrepreneur and founder of the incredibly stellar Virgin brand, Sir Richard Branson, is a prime example of this philosophy as he has proudly lorded over his fair share of great ideas, and very nebulous ones as well.[228] Although he has built amazing businesses worth billions in industries like music and aviation, he has had many other ideas which crashed shortly after take-off. Ideas such as Virgin Cola, Virgin Brides, Virgin Cars, and Virgin Digital Downloads all had much less success despite presumably being good ideas to Sir Richard at the time.[229] Arguably, he regards this approach to selecting business ideas as an essential part of progress towards finding the truly excellent ones, as he is often quoted as saying, "Do not be embarrassed by your failures, learn from them and start again."[230]

The iconic Steve Jobs, widely hailed as a genius, was similarly confidently in operating in a "hit and miss" mode when selecting and executing ideas. His successes are powerful and legendary, but buried in his resume are failed ideas that he strongly backed, created, or believed in. These public disasters include the Apple Lisa, The G4 Cube, Macintosh TV, The Apple III, and arguably even NeXT Computing.[231] Like Branson, failure to select and execute a winning idea never seemed to phase Jobs, as he was a firm believer in driving ideas via his instinct and willpower. In a 2005 Stanford University commencement speech, he implored the keen graduates to develop the conviction to trust their own mental algorithms when selecting ideas. He shared with the audience, "You can't connect the dots looking forward; you can only connect them looking backward. So you have to trust that the dots will somehow connect in your future. You have to trust in something, your gut, destiny, life, karma, whatever. This approach has never let me down, and it has made all the difference in my life."[232]

Perhaps it was this intoxicating conflict between this almost paranormal instinct, while still delivering a degree of commercial inconsistency, that occasionally drove skepticism from the market when he delivered a bold new idea to an expectant world. History correctly remembers Steve Jobs as a visionary, a purposeful marketer, and an innovator. However, when he took the stage to announce the now iconic iPod, the mac-fans swooned, but not everyone spontaneously applauded. The iPod was launched on October 23rd 2001, with a 5GB hard drive, ultra-compact design, and fire-wire exchange. The claim-to-fame was the seductively simple, "1,000 Songs in Your Pocket."[233] We know now that this was a total revolution for the industry. It propelled Apple into the portable music business, powered the success of iTunes, and set the stage for the incredible future of the iPhone. At the time, not every analyst could grasp the idea. It was criticised for being expensive, compatible only with Macs, just another MP3 player, and even a "gimmick" or a "toy."[234] While some analysts, like Forbes, were very positive, others like the NY Times forecast that it had a "limited potential audience" and Wired thought that it was uncompetitive given "many other digital music players on the market, many of them for a fraction of the price."[235]

Many analysts and experts in the financial markets were similarly not impressed with what Jobs proclaimed as a "fantastic" idea. On the day of the iPod launch, Apple stock closed at a lacklustre US$1.30 per share, and exactly one year later on October 23, 2002 Apple stock had declined and closed at only US$1.06.[236] It seemed that many experts failed to spot the iPod as a good idea, as Apple went on to sell 400 Million iPods across multiple formats and generations.[237] Perhaps this is evidence that Jobs' legendary instincts for ideas were unique and above mere mortals? Or perhaps, it is only proof that the analysts' have tools to expertly dissect and analyse the past, but can't accurately use their financial algorithms to predict disruptive good ideas?

Six years later, Jobs was back at it again with the launch of the iPhone on January 9th 2007. At the launch, he declared "The iPhone is a revolutionary, and magical product that is literally five years ahead of any other mobile phone. We are all born with the ultimate pointing device, our finger, and iPhone uses them to create the most revolutionary user interface since the mouse."[238] Even though their competitor, HP, had been employing touch screens on computing devices since 1983[239],

Apple was making bold claims to enter this new and exploding smart-phone category.

Even if the idea for the product wasn't entirely new, what was incredibly fresh was the design combined with the interface, and this truly excited people. This time, the market reaction seemed more positive, as the analysts were hungry and frothing to follow Jobs' newest ideas. Within a year of launch, Apple's value nearly doubled from US$13.22 per share to US$25.63.[240] Predictably, the entrenched competition, and some leading experts, still didn't share Jobs' vision and predicted their failure. Famously, the then stage-bounding and frenetic whooping CEO of Microsoft, Steve Ballmer, predicted "There's no chance that the iPhone is going to get any significant market share. No chance. It's a $500 subsidised item. They may make a lot of money, but if you actually take a look at the 1.3 billion phones that get sold, I'd prefer to have our software in 60 or 70 or 80% of them, then I would to have 2% or 3% which is what Apple might get."[241] How wrong was Ballmer? Over 2.2 billion iPhones have now been sold since sales began.[242]

Perhaps the people that got this idea the most wrong were the leaders at Nokia, who ironically had the most to lose. When the iPhone launched in 2007 they held a dominant 46% global market share. Six years later, when the flaccid phone company was sold to Microsoft in September 2013, they had collapsed to around 3% market share, and had lost 90% of their value.[243] Jorma Olllia, the CEO of Nokia who luckily departed the company in 2006, prior to the iPhone launch, apparently simultaneously championed Steve Jobs' "instinct" management philosophy while throwing a degree of shade at his subsequent CEO, Olli-Pekka Kallasvuo. He barbed on the demise of the company, "In the end, timing is all about intuition. It is never a democratic decision. The responsibility is the CEO's, and sensing the right time is the CEO's most important mission."[244] To paraphrase his observations, a CEO is ultimately paid the big bucks to use their mental algorithms to single-handily find, select, and invest in the best ideas. It could be argued that Branson, Jobs, and Ford's egos may agree with this accountability, and ultimately have justified this approach with the incredible legacies they have created. The issue is that when the entrepreneurial CEO gets it right, billions are made, however, when they select ideas erroneously, companies collapse and millions suffer with their personal careers and finances. As the world has seen, not only do many entrepreneurs get it completely wrong, they often believe that getting it wrong is an essential part of development and almost a badge of honour. They are effectively rolling the dice with good and bad ideas, and the risk and rewards for the planet is growing in parallel to the power of the technological ideas they are betting on.

This dynamic is both entrepreneurial history and current corporate and investor practice. The extensive venture capital and start-up community exists, in many ways, to minimise the risk of mainstream development and investment, and allow for mistakes to be made and bad choices to perish on the vine of ideas. In the start-up community, most ideas that see the light of day are ultimately rejected by the market. No matter how passionate and committed founders are to the powerful genesis of their breakthrough ideas, in the majority of cases, they are harshly judged by the market to be wrong, and sometimes drained of both their idea and capital. Statistics indicate that over 90% of startups ultimately fail, and 73% of venture capital funded startups also collapse.[245] Why they fail may be linked to the speed to market, cash flow and business management, rather than the core idea itself, but this still infers that even the most experienced and trained capital experts in selecting, vetting, and incubating new ideas, face a high degree of risk in predicting which idea will be a profitable game-changer. This is a major reason why a dominant business model of established companies is to outsource new ideas to the seductive and fashionable start-up ecosystem.

Any start-up possessing only marginal ideas will, and perhaps should, eventually fail, those that have great ideas at their core will succeed, generate revenue, profits and may even be on course to change the world. At this point, the major companies are then in a position to step in and acquire the proven business and de-risk idea selection. This is often a more preferable model than speculative investments in untested and unprofitable new ideas, and risking taking an expensive bath in the murky mud of the 90% failure rate.

For example, since inception in 2004, the innovators at Facebook have reportedly acquired no less than 72 companies at a disclosed acquisition cost of over US$23 Billion.[246] That is, on average, a new idea acquired every three months for over 16 years. Similarly, Apple and Amazon all have an extensive and impressive acquisition list. Companies with massive resources, like these tech-giants, already have enormous scale, talent, and reserves for their own internal extensive research and development programs. Yet, it appears to be an economically viable option to delegate the risk of idea selection to the open market and then handsomely skim across the industry for only the very best of ideas, proven with traction, and reward them accordingly.

Google, for many years, attempted a counter-culture approach to idea generation and proudly dedicated 20% of their employees' time to engaging in free range ideas. In their 2004 IPO statement, Google's co-founders Larry Page and Sergey Brin made this a key message with their statement. "We encourage our employees, in addition to their regular projects, to spend 20% of their time working on what they think will most benefit Google. This empowers them to be more creative and innovative. Many of our significant advances have happened in this manner."[247] It is true that some of Google's most powerful ideas such as Gmail and AdSense came for this program, but this bold idea has been widely reported to have since been shelved, as perhaps many more blanks were fired, then bulls eyes were hit in the process. By 2013, it was becoming less of a Google-focus as the company's management restructured more employee time on structured productivity, rather than randomised idea generation.[248] Simultaneously, Alphabet, the parent company of Google, has reportedly made over 230 acquisitions since 2001.[249] That is almost one new idea acquired every month from the market between 2001 and 2020, despite the "20% time for internal ideas" program running in parallel for a significant proportion of this time.

An industry-wide systemic approach of acquiring vetted ideas from the market, rather than internal creation of potential ideas, suggests something about the prevalence and challenges of creating truly "breakthrough" entrepreneurial ideas that birthed many of these technology behemoths to begin with. Visionary entrepreneurs may have created ideas that spawned billions, and in the process, enabled them to own global empires. However, these types of companies are apparently just as comfortable delegating back to the market to pick successful ideas for them, rather than solely deploying bespoke internal ideation structures to generate the future. Perhaps the fabled entrepreneurial leader's unique and gifted intuition is no more magical than the market? Or perhaps, it is driven by the nature of diverting corporate risk to satisfy shareholders and analysts who also struggle to calculate the prosperity of future ideas?

There are also incredible investors who have built their global reputation of having a mythical, zen like quality for selecting winning ideas. They cultivate a reputation of holding near-Jedi powers, as they effortlessly peer through the misty malaise of spreadsheets and PowerPoints, to pluck the most innovative rabbits from a sea of putrid hats. One such investor is the Billionaire, Masayoshi Son who is the CEO and Chairman of SoftBank and the Vision Fund, launched in 2017 with a ground-breaking war-chest of US$100 Billion dollars. The strategic intent behind the Vision Fund is to select innovative founders who are generating ideas, that will not only change the shape of technology today, but the fortunes of the next three hundred years.[250] The liquid companies behind this deep ocean of investment funds are the likes of Apple, Qualcomm, The Public Investment Fund of Saudi Arabia, and other legendary entrepreneurs such as Larry Ellison, who founded Oracle.[251] One possible reason these experienced investors may be drawn to delegate idea selection to the Vision Fund, is Masayoshi Son's global reputation to pan glints of gold from the turbulent waters of the idea market.

In early 2000, he was an active and aggressive investor in what was termed the 'dot.com boom'. He met, and quickly backed the founder of Alibaba, Jack Ma. Masayoshi Son made his investment decision with an incisive degree of intuition on the perceived inner steel of Jack Ma. He said about his meeting with him, "He had no business plan, zero revenue, but his eyes were very strong. I could tell from the way he talked, he has charisma, he has leadership."[252] Masayoshi Son's instincts were proven right as Jack Ma's drive and tenacity is now beyond question. That initial SoftBank investment of US$20M was worth over US$150 Billion by June 2020.[253] An incredible 7,500% increase.

Since the 2017 launch of the Vision Fund, Masayoshi Son and his team passionately invested over US$75 Billion in at least 88 companies.[254] This is an incredible surge of investment by any measurement. An average of US$2 billion invested in approximately 2.5 innovative ideas and founders every month for three years running. However, even the wisest Jedis will eventually make mistakes. Arriving too late on the investment scene with Uber, and what has been described as the "WeWork debacle" are two examples[255] of how idea selection, by even the best global visionaries, can go expensively south.

WeWork has gobbled over US$10 Billion[256] from the The Vision Fund, following the first investment arriving in 2017. WeWork was originally co-founded by Adam Neumann and Miguel McKelvey in New York in 2010 with a mission to revolutionise co-working office space by creating new environments for productivity, efficiency, and collaboration.[257] Seven years later, this idea had already amassed a valuation of US$17 Billion.[258] It was keenly seeking further capital for geographical expansion and acquisitions of their own so that they could take their collaboration idea beyond work-space and into schools and apartments.[259] By August 2017, SoftBank and the Vision Fund had confirmed an investment into WeWork, and newly created subsidiaries of US$4.4 billion. At the time, Masayoshi Son was expectedly of high praise for his new investment, and the entrepreneurial leadership of the CEO, Adam Neumann. He communicated to the press that WeWork is "leveraging the latest technologies and its own proprietary data systems to radically transform the way people work. Adam's unique vision and talented team have created a sharing platform that offers maximum flexibility and opportunity to creators of all types, from young entrepreneurs to large multinational companies. We are thrilled to support WeWork as they expand across markets and geographies and unleash a new wave of productivity around the world."[260] In 2018, he followed this positivity with the bold statement that WeWork was going to be his next "Alibaba".[261] He wasn't the only one to be seduced by Adam Neumann's hyper-brand of hype. In 2018, the respected, Time Magazine, listed WeWork as one of their "Genius Companies of the Year"[262], while the company peaked at a valuation of US$47 billion, and Bloomberg estimated that Neumann, alone, was worth US$14 Billion.[263]

However, by the end of 2019, just two years after the initial Vision Fund investment, the entrepreneurial shine of Adam Neumann's ideas were in a desperate decline. It was clear that rapid expansion did not easily translate into profitability, as the company was reportedly losing US$2 billion per year and needed to action a plan towards resolving this imbalance.[264] Neumann himself came under criticism for several questionable business practices, including, personally buying stakes in real-estate spaces that were then leased back to WeWork, and secondly, receiving US$5.9 million from the WeWork company to access the rights to the "We" brand name.[265] By September 2019, the paper on the planned Initial Public Offering was only becoming fit for the shredder. The company valuation plummeted. Mr Neumann unceremoniously left both the building, and the idea he helped both conceive and launch.[266] Additionally, the New York Times estimated that 4,000 to 5,000 employees would need to be cut from their jobs. The champagne and parties stopped flowing, and reality took hold.[267] In early 2020, Masayoshi Son announced that his Vision Fund had suffered an US$18 billion loss in the previous year, mainly due to write-downs on their investments, and had yet to conclude the capital raise on their 2nd Vision Fund aimed at securing another US$108 billion.[268] In a personal admission to Forbes magazine, he said "we paid too much valuation for WeWork, and we did too much believe in the entrepreneur."[269] His lucrative and legendary intuition to sense the true grit of an entrepreneurial idea had eluded him on this occasion, and it became costly for all involved.

Perhaps a great deal of this pain might have been avoided without reliance on any paranormal idea selection skills. As early as 2015, questions were being publicly raised about the WeWork business model, the robustness of their financial projections, and the potential valuation of the company.[270] In the same year, the Wall Street Journal was also raising the alarm that pre-IPO companies were commonly juggling with their forecast assumptions to excite investors with numbers that far exceed the true revenue and, therefore, would be falsely representing the growth in future revenue and profit.[271] In a comprehensive 2015 review of WeWork's investor materials, the influential media platform, BuzzFeed, argued that WeWork's ability to create immense value from a business model, primarily driven by office space leasing and subleasing, often had real-estate experts scratching their well-groomed heads in incredulity. Their opinion, was that by sprinkling the investor pitch with fashionable buzzwords like "sharing economy" and "asset light," WeWork was able to seduce investors, perhaps well beyond the time that their start-up phase should have concluded.[272]

Despite these published criticisms, within two years of the BuzzFeed report, The Vision Fund invested US$4.4 billion. At that time, the Wall Street Journal continued to echo BuzzFeed's concerns, stating that WeWork was predominately fuelled by "pixie-dust, showmanship, and tequila shots."[273] Just two years after this initial investment, BuzzFeed was arguably proven to be a better judge of this bad idea than The Vision Fund, as the WeWork valuation collapsed, the Founder had been evicted, and the reputations of many of the genius investors involved were besmirched to various degrees. The people that are currently getting the richest from this endeavour, are probably the lawyers involved in the ongoing deeply-embroiled lawsuits. In the meantime, don't feel too sorry for Mr Neumann. By April 2020, Bloomberg estimated that although his net-worth had plummeted by 97%, it was still in the ballpark of US$450 million as he remained a significant shareholder of WeWork.[274]

It also seems that his latest idea, that he still deserves billions of dollars more in compensation and benefits from WeWork and SoftBank, has also proved to be partially correct.[275] In a February 2021 settlement, it appears he may enjoy up to US$500 million in a share transaction.[276]

If it is true that 73% of venture capital funded companies ultimately collapse, perhaps this underscores how genuinely hard it is to pick a good idea, and nurture it to ultimate success. Given the level of risk involved, expert investors, if they make enough bets on new ideas, will eventually be rewarded if a minority pay out in a massive way despite the accumulative cost of calculated failures. Especially if their proprietary "gut feeling" can attract capital of astronomical size. Indeed, based on entrepreneurial folklore, failures and losses are an essential precursor for future success. However, if this system is responsible for the next generation of idea selection, that will ultimately help shape our society's future, how many ideas will it get wrong, or simply miss, before they eventually get it right? What is the cultural and societal cost of getting it wrong as the power and impact of technology morphs and scales?

There are many rose-tinted innovation gurus, that feed off the speaking circuit, and lavishly polish the crowns of entrepreneurs while praising them with the rare ability to frame the future. In reality, while some are incredibly gifted in summoning the odd-entrepreneurial genius out of a bottle, very few of them have a full-proof system for continuously pre-selecting winning ideas. This means that our society can't always confidently rely on delegating our future to the jitters of the capital market or even the world's best entrepreneurs and investors to get ideas right for our planet, 100% of the time. The system is designed to run on fuzzy logic.

Any inherent flaws in relying on entrepreneurial oracles may have always been a glitch that was hiding in the system. For example, the legendary Henry Ford, who revolutionised mass production and the automotive industry, may have also selected some very terrible ideas. He has been accused of holding disgustingly Anti-Semitic ideals, and via the Ford Germany manufacturing plant, a supporter of the Nazi party in the lead up to World War II.[277] In 1938, he became the the first American recipient of the Nazi Party's highest honour for foreigners, The Grand Cross of the Supreme Order of the German Eagle, created in 1937 by Adolf Hitler himself.[278] The Henry Ford Museum of Innovation lists many important and distinguished accolades given to Henry Ford for his contribution to the industry. However, this particular award curiously does not seem to be included in their proud scroll of honours.[279] In 1940, it is also alleged that Ford confirmed to the automobile editor of The Associated Press that he placed blame for the war raging across Europe, firmly at the feet of the Jews, and not the Nazis. "I still think this is a phoney war, made by the international Jewish banker." He allegedly said.[280] At this time, Ford was perhaps the richest person on the planet, yet, if he did say these words, he was wrong in every possible way.[281] As our technology becomes more powerful, the volume of ideas rises, economies become more connected and the speed of globalising ideas accelerates closer to light speed, the consequences of getting ideas wrong must also proportionally increase. Tolerance for a high degree of failure is not only baked into the current idea selection system, but proudly lauded as a beautiful part of the "fail fast and break things" mentality. Can we continue to tolerate the level of risk that is conjoined with this model? A key question remains, is there anyone, or anything, that might be better tasked with selecting the very best ideas to propel our civilisation forward, decrease risk and increase the probability of growing prosperity for many generations to come?

CHAPTER 9

THE IDEA ILLUSION.

When it comes to ideas, research indicates that the majority of people will select information that reinforces their beliefs, rather than those that might challenge them. We often like to feel that we are right, even if we are potentially wrong, or even ignorant of the facts. In a meta-data analysis of almost 8,000 people and across 91 separate studies, the Universities of Florida and Illinois showed that when given the choice of reading content that supports an idea that they already think is true, or selecting content that contradicts it, and therefore risk dismantling their own beliefs, 67% of people will choose to reinforce their position and not prise open the very uncomfortable lid of change. They found that this was especially true for beliefs related to religious, political, and moral ideas.[282]

As a species, when it comes to ideas, we take comfort in staying firmly in our own lane. After all, many of these "lanes" such as politics, religion, and morality are our cherished ideas which we have intellectually vetted and then internalised over many years as personal dogma. In many psychological experiments, this familiarity and connection to an idea is known as the "mere-exposure" effect. This is widely credited to the 1960s social psychologist, Robert Zajonc[283] but has also been shown in studies as far back as the 1870s. The research shows that people are inclined to develop a preference for ideas merely because they are familiar with them. That familiarity to an idea, breeds through direct interaction, when it is repeated to a person on a consistent and continual basis. There is complexity built within this model. The length of exposure, time between exposures, and what state the human mind is in during the exposure, all influence and alter potential outcomes.

Advertising and marketing have often operated on a sophisticated frequency model to take advantage of this instinctive and evolved human condition of accepting primacy ideas, but they do it at a colossal scale. Every day, everywhere on the planet, companies spend billions of dollars, creating trillions of messages, for new ideas that utilise data-driven, real-time analytics, to repeatedly feed consumers these messages designed to take advantage of the "mere-exposure" effect. In fact, 98.5% of Facebook's US$70 billion revenue in 2019 came from advertising revenue that arguably, digitally leverages this basic human psychological phenomena.[284] A high proportion of a modern advertising platform's revenue usually comes from the distribution of mundane, often trivial and intrusive ideas, such as a new set of steak knives, anti-dandruff shampoo, or a miraculous exercise machine, specially designed to enthusiastically rust under the bed in perpetual hibernation, post-purchase. Other content communicated on these massive online and offline platforms, will be dedicated to more vital and long-term ideas, critical for society to wrestle with and select outcomes. This can include ideas such as climate change, diversity, equal rights, or social change. In the 2020 US Presidential election, over US$6.8 billion was assembled to persuade voters whether to think left or right when considering ideas essential to the future of the nation.[285] Persuasiveness and advertising are not limited to the mediocrity of household detergents, it is deployed strategically, and expertly, against the most important ideas that affect the prosperity and strength of society.

Familiarity with a new idea is often built from high frequency, supraliminal communication, via paid and unpaid media, or even in direct conversation with influencers and friends. In this mechanism, people generally acknowledge that the idea, even if they subsequently adopt it, was not originally created by them. They often recognise that these ideas have been externally presented to them, for consideration and review. The advertising communication is, by default, designed to be as obvious as possible, sometimes painfully so, and the correct source of the idea is boldly attributed, and even desperately defined, by a brand, organisation or a political party. Advertising and communication in this format are often considered to be annoying and invasive, even if it is ultimately effective at increasing familiarity, triggering the "mere-exposure" effect and therefore generating an increased acceptance of the promoted idea. It is of course possible to create unique, compelling, and effective communication, that requires significantly less investment in frequency for acceptance. However, generally, the communication industry defaults to the more common denominator of hardcore and repetitive sales messages to drive familiarity with an idea and infiltrate the mind rather than to entertain it. Almost 80% of people agree that the most annoying form of commercial idea communication is telemarketing, and over 70% agree that pop-up online advertising comes in a grating second. It's one of the reasons that over 200 million people have already installed ad-blockers on their mobile devices costing the publishing industry approximately US$35 billion a year in lost revenue.[286]

As a general rule, the majority of people do not really want to be sold to. Our species often feel that we should consciously resist overt sales attempts and believe that we are intrinsically equipped to make our own decisions, and are actually quite good at it. Unfortunately, humans are not as in complete control of our decisions as our monkey-minds have continually led us to believe. Ideas are more subversive, slippery, and subliminal than we think. They infiltrate, overtake, and conduct silent coups as we are sit, slack-jawed, in front of our screens. While the conscious mind is actively slamming the phone down on the insistently oblivious telemarketing caller, the exact same mind is secretly and passively collecting and storing ideas from multiple external stimuli for future use. This shapes how we select ideas, and is actively fooling our conscious mind into believing that we are the brilliant creators of the building blocks of ideas that had silently slithered into our subconscious.

Like secret sleeper cells waiting patiently for their orders, so they can be unleashed with either beauty or havoc on our hearts, minds and, communities.

Scientists have replicated the "mere-exposure effect" and how it operates on a subliminal basis on multiple occasions. In one study, the researchers from the University of Pittsburgh, arranged for four different women (but of physically similar appearances) to attend a university lecture, at varying amounts throughout the term. The first woman did not attend any classes, the next attended five times, the third attended ten times, and the final woman attended the most, fifteen times. Their role was to not engage with any other students, just to be present in class to simulate subliminal frequency, and test whether the mere-exposure effect works sub-consciously. At the end of the semester, the students in the class were shown photographs of each of the women and asked to rank them on multiple scales, such as attractiveness. The results clearly supported the mere-exposure effect, especially when it came to perceived attractiveness. The woman, who attended the most classes was judged by the class more positively and as more attractive than the woman who hadn't attended any classes.[287]

In another study, pre-school children were shown TV programs that had actors from multi-cultural backgrounds. After viewing, they were subsequently more likely to agree that they would also play in groups with children from diverse backgrounds, at a much higher level than children who did not watch these same programs.[288] Whether it is music, language, art, or relationships a great deal of research consistently indicates that there is a correlation between subliminal frequency and a positive inclination towards an idea.[289] This has an impact on the daily choices of the music and movies we enjoy, but more importantly, it impacts the people we gravitate towards, and those we fall in love with and build futures together.

Proximity naturally increases the frequency and this then amplifies the gravity of the mere-exposure effect. It is perhaps one of the underlying reasons that, according to Pew Research, 38% of people marry from their immediate social and work groups.[290] Shared values, beliefs, and even economic status will certainly play an objective and conscious role, but deliciously hiding underneath all of this interaction, is the subconscious beat of the mere-exposure effect. It helps to convince our minds that true love was divine destiny, when in reality, cupid may have been sparked simply by the chance repeated frequency of meeting people around an office cubicle or the coffee machine.

Consciously, we don't readily accept this idea, but the research indicates that it can, and does happen as a natural part of our psychology. Our senses constantly and involuntarily collect subliminal information from multiple sources. Body language, background images, sounds, textures, and scents all inadvertently trigger our subconscious to store this information as data points. These can be later reassembled by our conscious mind and emerge as an idea that we have been fooled into thinking that we created all on our own.

To illustrate how internal ideas can be influenced by external subliminal interference, the British mentalist and illusionist, Darren Brown conducted an experiment to manipulate the minds of the most creative people he could find. His mission was to get them to generate ideas that he had previously secretly subconsciously planted.[291] His construct was to challenge leading senior Creative Directors from an international advertising agency to create a poster campaign (the key imagery and a slogan) for a new chain of taxidermy stores, in just twenty minutes. The advertising professionals are proudly and clearly under the illusion that they are using their own free will, intellect, and highly-valued, and handsomely paid creativity, to generate ideas to match his brief. Darren Brown also provided them with his own preconceived creative ideas, sealed in an envelope and handed to them to guard for tamperproof safekeeping. The result? At the end of the twenty-minute test, the fresh and independent ideas of the advertising professionals are almost an exact match of the ones that Darren Brown predicted that they would create. This generates the illusion that he has paranormal abilities, to either predict the future or read minds. The truth, however, is that the challenge is a precisely engineered, but natural outcome of subliminal messaging and the mere-exposure effect.

After the experiment is completed, Darren Brown reveals to the audience that during the car journey, he had organised for the Creative Directors to travel to the experiment, they were subtly, expertly, and constantly bombarded with images, messages, and information that subconsciously predisposed them to generate the very ideas the famous Mentalist desired and had pre-determined for them. The required Taxidermy slogans are deftly printed on passing taxis, pedestrian t-shirts, and other signage on the street, as the Creative Directors quickly drove by. The "predicted" key creative images are similarly deliberately and frequently adorned on buildings, balloons, shop windows, and even as toys carried by people walking on the street. This information is passively absorbed by the unsuspecting subconscious minds of the Creative Directors watching the world go by in their car. On arrival, they are given the challenge to create something new and original, instead, they unknowingly regurgitate what has been artificially injected into the synapses of their brains by the mentalist beforehand. What their conscious-self perceives as their own free will, creativity, and spontaneity is, in truth, pre-orchestrated, predictable, and already lurking in their subconscious, waiting to emerge as an idea that they believe they created and are in control of. Their incredulity on how their internationally awarded and lauded creativity could ever be so entirely and eerily predicted is only matched by the uniformed predictability of their bearded-stubble, black t-shirts and thick-rimmed glasses.

It is a further indication that when it appears that our mental algorithms are majestically generating fresh ideas, drawn from a floating cloud of inspiration, they are simply re-arranging our sub-consciously stored observations of reality. This happens to all of humanity every day, to various degrees. What we constantly regard as the marvel of our creativity is often heavily influenced and pre-determined by the mundane cacophony of the subliminal stimulus that surrounds us. It's inescapable, automatic, and irrefutable. Our freshest creative ideas that we share on calls, presentations, and meetings are sometimes no more original than those of a domesticated parrot, squawking swear words they mistakenly and randomly overheard. Like the parrot, humanity is often none-the-wiser to the true source of the profanities, yet we seek to take credit for their conscious creations. What ultimately may make our individual squawks unique is that everyone is absorbing vastly different random stimulus and storing it in their own sub-conscious data sets, for their distinct mental algorithms to later re-shuffle and re-assemble into a spontaneous new idea.

This is not the only mechanism that fools the conscious part of our minds into being mistakenly under the impression that it's in full control of the ideas we create. Apart from frequency and involuntary stored subliminal images, we are also silently influenced in our choices and reactions by what is commonly known as the Placebo Effect, derived from the Latin word "to please". It describes how the mind can transform an event, that is only perceived to be true, into a physical reality. Although not termed "Placebo" until the 1920s, it was perhaps first examined in the late 1700s by scientists as famous as Benjamin Franklin. In 1784, he concocted an experiment designed to debunk claims that there was a natural force that people called "Animal Magnetism", which was thought to accelerate healing if applied in just the right way. His results concluded that if objects were only "perceived" to have been magnetised by this mythical force they would still have as many positive responses as the force itself. His conclusion was that it was human imagination, and not the supernatural, that was responsible for any healing benefit received from the magnetised object.[292]

A few years later in 1799, the British physician, John Haygarth built upon these studies with his own investigation. He wanted to expose the true effectiveness of a newly marketed miracle medical device that had recently been launched by an American physician and surgeon, Elisha Perkins.[293] A few years prior, Perkins had patented what he believed to be a revolutionary new device designed to cure inflammation, rheumatism, and other pains such as headaches. This device had gained a degree of popularity and credibility through the publication of his book, combined with support from some reputable institutions. Even the US President, George Washington, reportedly bought a set.[294] The miracle device was in-fact merely long, thin, metal brass rods that were branded "Perkins Tractors". His very novel idea was that these rods were to be placed on the affected area of the body for twenty minutes, and in that time the tractors would alleviate the condition by drawing harmful "electrical fluid" out of the patient which was causing the discomfort. Unfortunately for Perkins, his innovative tractors certainly didn't cure all critical illnesses, as he soon died in New York of yellow fever in late 1799, before his fortune could be both made or enjoyed from them.

However, Haygarth still wanted to test the efficacy of these tractors as he believed them to be a complete sham. He devised an experiment where the original metal Perkins tractors were tested on patients, versus fabricated wooden versions he had separately prepared. In 1800, he announced his findings in his book "On the Imagination as a Cause and as a Cure of Disorders of the Body." What he found astounded him. Both the wooden and metal tractors were equally effective medicinal devices, despite having no foundation in pharmacology or science. In fact, 80% of patients with rheumatism indicated that his fabricated wooden tractors assisted them with pain relief.[295] He concluded that this must be due to the patient's imagination and the power of suggestion, rather than the intrinsic design and composition of the tractors. If people were presented with an idea, suggesting they would receive relief of pain by taking a defined course of action, then pain relief could be manifested by the mind and independently measured, simply by taking that course of action. Mere belief in an idea was enough to turn that idea into a physical reality. Haygarth extended his findings to more than just medical devices, and proposed that this was perhaps why doctors that are more famous are often seemingly better at curing illness than their lesser-known counterparts. He suggested that if a patient thought that a doctor was talented and highly skilled, this may be enough to further enhance the benefits from their treatment. He was centuries ahead of his time with this insight into how ideas create true reality inside the human mind.

It was actually the American Anaesthesiologist, Henry Beecher in 1955 who cemented the Placebo Effect into mainstream science. He publicised the results of fifteen trials in the prestigious Journal of the American Medical Association, indicating that taking medicine under the guise of a Placebo Effect, could deliver up to 35% more efficacy than taking no compounds at all.[296] Although there were shortcomings in this research, the Placebo Effect has since been further studied and replicated countless times, and is now a confirmed part of modern medicinal research.

When a new drug or compound is undergoing clinical trials, its effectiveness is commonly placed against a placebo to prove that it's statistically more effective than just the mere suggestion and belief that the drug will provide a cure. In double-blind tests, one group is given the new compound, one group is given a placebo and told it is an effective compound, while others are perhaps given nothing. The results are subsequently dissected and analysed by the authorities. If the compound doesn't beat the placebo, it is unlikely to proceed with approval and is potentially shelved. Due to their proven effectiveness, placebos themselves can be used as effective treatment methodologies in some conditions to treat non-specific symptoms of chronic pain, depression, and anxiety. A UK study of over 1,700 General Practitioners reported that over 97% had prescribed some form of placebo at least once in their careers.[297]

There is a degree of complexity to how our minds process and react to a placebo. Research indicates that colour dramatically changes how we perceive the effectiveness of a medical idea, and therefore, the true effectiveness of a compound. Red pills improve the placebo effect for pain relief, blue is associated with reducing sleeping disorders, and yellow placebo pills reduce anxiety more effectively than other colours. The form factor of treatment also has a perception hierarchy. Placebo capsules are more potent than tablets, needles are more powerful than capsules, and sophisticated, electronic placebo devices seemingly beat the placebo injection.[298] Intriguingly, placebos may still have a positive impact on our bodies, even if the patient is told that it is only a placebo and is consciously aware that it has no active pharmacological components. Research from Harvard Medical School indicates that the idea of taking a pill, performing the ritual of consumption, and following the advice of an expert may, on occasion, be enough to change the reality of an illness.[299]

Astoundingly, further research has confirmed John Haygarth's initial instinct, that even our perception on the quality of the care-giver alters the power of the placebo. Research conducted by the Stanford University Professor, Dr Alia Drum, indicates that the patient's idea as to the perceived professionalism of a Doctor, can have an impact on how their bodies respond to treatment. Placebos administered to patients by doctors who show empathy, credibility, professionalism, and skill will measurably outperform placebos prescribed by doctors who demonstrate the opposite.[300] The actual idea of a doctor is therefore critically important to how our physical bodies respond to treatment. Clean white lab coats, professional settings, framed certificates, attention to detail, sophisticated jargon, and even the doctor's body language and eye contact, can help influence our sub-conscious minds, and positively impact how our body responds to a placebo drug. This effect may even extend into cultural differences as the placebo effect apparently has different impacts in different cultures. This may influence how severe or critical an illness is perceived to be within a culture and effect how those individuals respond to a placebo.[301] Bizarrely, this effect stretches to what is known as placebo surgeries. Some recent research studies indicate that up to 50% of patients that simply experience the ritual of a surgery, and believe the surgery has taken place, may then report a positive improvement in their condition, even though no physical change in the body has occurred.[302]

Our minds absorb these placebo ideas, and then our subconscious turns these ephemeral thoughts into objective, measurable, and physical reality. How and why this actually occurs is less understood, as the phenomenon covers such a wide range of territories and inflictions. Most research indicates that it may be a neurobiological response linked to brain biology, and the release of powerful chemical neurotransmitters to either promote or block a physiological response based on the perceived stimulus.[303] Placebos, and their opposite, stimulus which causes a negative effect called "Nocebos" seem to have the strongest impact on neurological and emotional conditions. They also have limitations as they don't have a measurable influence on other types of physical ailments like infections and cancers. This implies that our physical acceptance and response to an idea may be as shaped and influenced by involuntary and sub-conscious brain chemistry as much as, or in partnership with, our rational, conscious analysis of the idea and the scientifically tested pharmacology. It's important to stress that a placebo is not an imaginary effect, but a real-world measurable impact, manifested into existence by our psychology.

While the Placebo Effect has been extensively studied in medicine, their impact on psychology is not limited to this one sector. A broad cross-section of ideas that we follow or accept on a daily basis may also be impacted by placebos. Many things we are constantly stimulated by, such as colour, music, and the environment can all effect our emotions and physiological response. Placebos can be orally taken, visual, or even audible cues. Research indicates that wine is perceived to taste sweeter while listening to Beethoven,[304] sweet foods taste better on white plates, and both weight and colour effect how much we savour and enjoy all kinds of foods and products.[305] Indeed, a customer enjoying a meal in a restaurant, with predominately blue lighting, will statistically eat less then in any other environment.[306] Music can even be a proven pain reliever, especially when it is music that we love and are familiar with. Research has even indicated that music can reduce the perceived "heart-break" felt when a loving relationship has ended.[307]

Incredibly, the placebo effect can fool an athlete into performing at a level they did not think was possible, by as much as 3% higher. This may not sound meaningful for a competitive advantage, but as Chris Beedie from the School of Psychology at the University of Kent, who conducted the research in professional cyclists articulated, "In elite athlete terms, 3% is the difference between winning an Olympic medal and not making the top ten."[308] Indeed, the widely recognised and often statistically relevant concept of "home-ground advantage" in sports may be due to an innate belief from the athletes that there is an advantage to being at home, which then triggers a placebo effect and delivers the energy and focus to step-up and win.[309]

The Placebo Effect influences the effectiveness of medicine, hunger, purchasing decisions, emotions, and physical performance across the human race. It is not surprising that it plays a central part of all items and ideas that are marketed to consumers everywhere. Extra-strong tablets are packaged in bold red for greater effectiveness. We perceive a higher degree of luxury and performance from an item when we pay full price.[310] The entire concept of brand recognition also operates as a placebo effect to a certain degree. A beer, for example, is perceived to taste better when from a popular brand, than the same beer stripped of its identity and drunk from a bland bottle.[311]

There is no reason why this placebo impact isn't transferred to important issues impacting society like politics, economics, racism, and diversity. Many of the politicians and groups that are selling ideas to a community, consistently behave, act, and market themselves exactly as brands. The symbolic iconography and rituals that they leverage to build their image and agenda may similarly have a Placebo Effect on all of the viewing population and influence decisions.

Unnervingly, when the most important economic, security, and political ideas for the future of our culture are marketed like beers or a soft-drink, we will be more likely to accept the idea when it is presented in a context that triggers either a positive or negative placebo effect in our subconscious. It can create a physical neurological response that attracts or repels us from the idea. Our conscious minds may believe it is actively listening and crunching the facts to produce a rational analytical decision on either a policy, or whether to support a President, but it may be that part of our response is simply the Placebo Effect, pulling on our mental strings and making us dance to the tune of a chemical neurotransmission. Like an athlete lunging across the finish line, placebos could make the difference between winning and losing an election through subtly influencing voter support in closely contested State or National elections. This may, in turn, change the lives of many people in the community and, in the worse case scenario, such as a policy to pursue armed combat, may ultimately mean life or death for thousands.

An example of this exact scenario is in 2003, when the George W. Bush Administration selected the then US Secretary of State, Colin Powell, to make the case at the United Nations for the idea that Saddam Hussein, and his regime, were harbouring Weapons Of Mass Destruction (WMD), and brazenly and illegally defying the will of the international community. This was portrayed as an imminent threat, in a "Post September 11 World" and thus an armed invasion of Iraq by the "Collation of the Willing" was essential, moral, and inevitable. The presentation was, ostensively for the diplomats in the room, but arguably, it was also designed for the media to re-broadcast it to millions of people and spread the fear of Saddam Hussein, the threat of WMD's, and assist to justify an invasion of Iraq.

Almost two decades has passed since this pivotal presentation, and Colin Powell now laments it as a "great intelligence failure" and a "permanent stain" on his record, yet he still supports the invasion itself.[312] It is now widely reported that the contents of his famous speech created a significantly false narrative on the capabilities of the Iraqi regime at the time.[313] It's now apparent that the idea that Iraq had significant stockpiles of WMD's wasn't true, but perhaps it was an essential idea for the world to believe in, to garner enough justification to start a war. In a 2016 interview, when Powell was specifically asked why he was selected by President Bush to sell the idea of WMD's in Iraq to the UN, part of his explanation underscored his perceived ability to influence the audience; "I think he thought I had credibility to deliver a speech, and it would be believable." He told the press.[314]

At the time, Colin Powell had an 85% approval rating, and was seen as moderate voice in a relatively hawkish administration.[315] Gallup poll data also suggested that 63% of Americans preferred Colin Powell to make foreign policy decisions compared to 26% for President Bush. In many ways, he was a very credible diplomat in the eyes of the media, voters, and the United Nations. Science has separately proven that a trusted and believable "brand" that can power a Placebo Effect, is in many ways, a perfect vehicle to present an idea, similarly to how we are more likely to accept knowledge from a doctor in a white coat, and prefer a beer with a trusted label. Perhaps the words that flowed from the pages of that presentation were more palatable and believable because they came from Colin Powell's placebo laced lips? Given his status, track record, respect, and appeal as a sensible, moderate "brand", it is possible that his presence and delivery triggered an involuntary Placebo Effect in the minds of the members of the United Nations, and everyone who listened to his speech, around the world. This could have potentially resulted in a physiological response to physically reduce objections and increase support from diplomats and the media. Imagine if the more aggressive, polarising, Republican Vice President, Dick Cheney, had made the case? What response would he have received from the various stakeholders and governments?

The presentation itself was presumptively titled "Iraq. Failing To Disarm", and was interspersed with potentially deliberate signals of trust that may have triggered placebos. This included how the presentation slides were consistently designed in solid "placebo calming" blue, with the typeface for the content in "placebo active" yellow.[316] Combined, this iconography may have helped to convey a sense of measured, considered, yet purposeful action. Curiously, the slides don't appear to the audience with the definitively American-centric "red, white and blue/stars and stripes" iconography, and therefore subconsciously appears more bipartisan and inclusive to the diplomats and the viewers. Indeed, across all 43 slides presented, no visual credit is given to the United States of America directly. Conveniently, the United Nations' brand colour is also a "neutral" blue, and the slides mirror this palate and may subconsciously appear more like they were prepared or vetted by the UN itself and feel like they stemmed from a more representative, unified, or balanced view.

The presentation is largely devoid of all signs of humanity, the peaceful people of Iraq are totally absent from the slides. As far as Powell's presentation is concerned, they don't exist, and barely scrape a mention. "Weapon" is mentioned over sixty times in the speech, and the innocent Iraqi citizens are sadly only mentioned once.[317] The lesson here, is that if you do want to start a war, best not showcase or describe schools, hospitals, and peaceful families that you want to save. Better to stoke the fires of fear and the need for pre-emptive retaliation. In fact, faces are rarely shown throughout the presentation, except for one section which focuses strongly on the alarmist case (and even at the time, dubious case) of an emerging terrorist cell in Iraq that were connected to a global network of terror. Here, the menacing images of seven named terrorists repeatedly and defiantly stare back at the UN diplomats. Colin Powell makes the case that this worldwide cabal of terrorists was now lurching towards Iraq, looking to leverage the WMD's held by the regime. He personalises this by delivering the horse-head of fear directly into the bed of the audience by connecting these evil faces to a US Diplomat,

Mr Lawrence Fowley, who was murdered by terrorists one year earlier. De-humanising the entire presentation, except for specific people that were repeatedly presented as murderers, and presumably must deserve to die, could have potentially had a placebo effect on the audience to stiffen resolve for armed conflict.

The last element of placebo design in this presentation, was the dramatisation of the witness descriptions, of transports designed to carry the deadly biological weapons. While Colin Powell clearly states that they have multiple eye-witness accounts of these vehicles[318], we need to assume that they either did not have any true or verified images, or did not wish to share them. Instead, they showcased highly illustrated concepts of how these weaponised trucks may have appeared. Interestingly, from a placebo perspective, these illustrations don't place the artificial images of vehicles carrying deadly pathogens, on a neutral background, or perhaps sitting on a more practical tarmac or asphalt, the natural home of an eighteen-wheeled truck. Instead, these massive biological weapon-carriers are illustrated to be sitting on, what looks like, Iraqi dessert sand. The vehicles have sharp and dark shadows to project a clear impression that they are operating in a sunny, hot, and dry environment. This echos the common perception of Iraq after the the 1990 invasion known as "Operation Desert Storm". This clear use of a desert environment in these images sub-consciously emphasises the point that these biological weapon-carriers are bespoke to an environment like Iraq, and therefore, must be based there and a present threat to the world.

Did all of these audio and visual potential placebos have an unconscious effect on the diplomats receiving the presentation and the millions around the world that viewed the coverage? Were they accidental or deliberate marketing techniques similar to those used to get consumers to buy toothpaste and toilet paper? We may never know the truth, or if there was any degree of Placebo Effect from the presentation. While Colin Powell's compelling presentation did not reverse many countries' position on Iraq, his words and images potentially succeeded in building additional support and justification for the invasion amongst the forty-six countries involved in the "Coalition Of The Willing" such as the United Kingdom and Australia. It arguably gave them the credibility they domestically sought to justify their unilateral decisions, outside of the UN charter, to their own nations. It was also critical in generating US voter support for an invasion.

Polls in 2003 indicated that while the majority of Americans already supported an invasion, more than half of them said they could still change their minds one way or another. Additionally, nine in ten Americans said that the UN presentation was going to be important in determining their position on the invasion.[319] The Washington Post conducted a poll in the days following the historic UN speech. Their findings indicated that Colin Powell's presentation did have an impact. 50% of people subsequently felt that the US had a clear case for war, and only 19% were against invasion.[320] Surprisingly, in 2015, and more than a decade after Colin Powell's speech, despite precisely zero WMD's ever being found in Iraq, 51% of people in the US who identify as Republicans, still believe that American soldiers found WMD's in Iraq.[321]

The contents of Colin Powell's speech still powerfully echos across time, as the idea is firmly lodged in the American publics' mind. Perhaps, as there was never a countering speech, given with the same seniority, presence, conviction, coverage, staging, and then amplification to confirm the opposite was actually true, and admit the grave mistakes. It can be argued that the erroneous ideas contained in the Colin Powell presentation and broadcast to the world are now considered to be more truthful by many Republicans than the objectively true fact that there was no WMD's in Iraq.

In his memoirs, Colin Powell confessed his pivotal role and dramatic impact on history: «There would have been no war in Iraq had then President George W. Bush, and his councillors, understood that Saddam Hussein did not possess any functioning unconventional weapons."[322] Believing in the idea that Saddam Hussein was secretly wielding WMD's, was an essential step on the path to adopting the much more perilous and deadly idea of invading Iraq. Depressingly, after the President Bush Administration successfully made the case for this idea, war, death and chaos flowed in Iraq like a brutal blood river breaking through a dam. Over 4,400 US and Coalition soldiers were killed, over 31,000 brave soldiers were injured, and estimates on total deaths for Iraqi soldiers, terrorists, insurgents, and civilians exceed 600,000 over the last fifteen years.[323] Of the seven terrorists identified by Powell in his presentation, two were eventually killed by the US. One in Iraq[324], and one by drones in Pakistan[325]. Two others served prison sentences in France[326] [327], and the three others are still at large, potentially in Syria, or Iran. Perhaps innocently so? The facts surrounding their guilt are not clear or transparently defined. Over US$2 trillion was spent on the Iraq war, which is almost US$8,000 for each and every American tax payer.[328] In hindsight, it wasn't even a good idea at the time, despite the tragedy of September 11th.

However, on a much more positive and optimistic front, former US Vice-President, Dick Cheney's estimated net-worth has grown to a comfortable US$110 million[329], and there has never been a public enquiry into why the ideas in Colin Powell's presentation, based on the information provided by the CIA, was arguably completely, and perhaps even deliberately, misleading.[330] Similarly, Tony Blair, the former UK Prime Minister, who strongly advocated for the idea of invasion, and committed British troops into combat, has luckily also done very well. He now has a net-worth estimated to be around US$60 million[331], and reportedly commands a fee of up to US$430,000 for a brisk, yet inspiring twenty minute speech, where he may share his pearls of wisdom about how he wrestled with vexing ideas of faith and morality in the face of global challenges.[332] Or perhaps these outcomes might only be regarded as positive for these particular politicians, and not for the people of Iraq or the brave and honourable soldiers who fought on their instructions. It's all a matter of perspective on how you judge a good idea.

What percentage of other critical and important decisions by Politicians, Generals, Judges, Business Leaders, and everyday voters are affected by the hidden hand of these subconscious, seductive and subliminal placebo mechanisms? Especially on ideas that are finely balanced, subjective, or nuanced but vitally important to our culture and civilisation. Are major decisions influenced by our rational conscious intellect but also invisibly nudged by our involuntary psychological and neurobiological responses due to a Placebo Effect? When we finally decide to support an important idea or a charismatic politician, how can we be sure, as a society, that it's the right idea, chosen through the analytical control of our conscious minds, or was it just tipped slightly in that direction by an involuntary response, driven by neurotransmitters and manipulated by external context, imagery, suggestions, or a Placebo Effect? An old proverb would encourage humanity when faced with such a dichotomy to "go with your gut." Unfortunately, that too may be contributing to the illusion of who truly owns our ideas as our guts definitely seems to have a mind of its own.

CHAPTER 10

THE IDEA COLONY.

In truth, the human body does not entirely consist of human cells alone. We are hosts to an entire universe of other organisms that inhabit our skin, mouth, nasal, and intestinal tracts. These microbes are collectively called "microbiota" and, unlike viruses and other bacteria, they are a natural and essential part of our metabolism and health. The Human Microbiota Project (a consortium of leading international laboratories) has recently suggested that there may be up to 10,000 different species of microbiota[333], living both on and inside us in a symbiotic relationship with our digestive, immune, and nervous systems called the "microbiome". Most of these organisms have yet to be characterised by science, and their role and benefits are not fully understood. To explore the microbiome is like a submarine expedition, diving to the depth of the Mariana Trench and shining fluorescent light for the first time on a massive and beautifully complex ecosystem and watch stunning new forms of life swim by. Although, in this case, the submarine is a microscope and the Mariana Trench is usually the slightly less-romantic and much less pristine, tracts of the human bowels. The microbiota are microscopic, so despite their vast numbers in their trillions, they may only constitute a maximum of 6% of our total body weight, or between 1 and 3kg.[334] This may not sound significant, but when you consider that the human brain is approximately 1.5kg, this then offers some perspective on the sheer quantity of other organisms we are all currently carrying, feeding, and allowing to multiply in and on our bodies.

Incredibly, when this volume is measured from a genetic material perspective, their total presence is far greater. Recent research on the human genome indicates that each person has approximately 22,000 protein-coding genes. In comparison, researchers now estimate that the microbiota in our bodies may contribute up to eight million unique protein-coding genes.[335] In other words, within every single person on the planet, microbiota genes may outnumber human genes by up to 360 times. This type of relationship can sometimes be mistakenly called a 'Supraorganism", probably because it sounds like a cool character from a Marvel comic. This is not strictly correct, as that term describes a shared co-existence of a single species, such as an ant colony. The type of relationship that humans are inexorably involved with may be more accurately termed as a "Holobiont". In this type of relationship, a "Host" provides the environment for other organisms, collectively termed as "bionts", to then inhabit the same space.[336] The total combined genome of host and bionts is called the hologenome. Another example of a holobiont partnership is a vibrant coral reef, where different species co-exist and interact together within the same living structure and space.

If a scientist from another planet was to coldly study just the blended pool of DNA from humanities' hologenome, they may conclude that we are essentially more microbiota than human. In many aspects, a holobiont community can operate and evolve as if it was one single entity, where separation is either impossible, or may result in negative consequences, or the death of the bionts, or even the host organism. In humans, a significant amount of the most essential microbiome living within us will be inherited at birth, from the maternal side. This may come through breast milk, or as the baby passes through the birth canal, its skin will naturally collect microbiota from the vaginal wall.[337] So our microbiome is, in many senses, inherited across generations, potentially to support, aid, or influence our survival and evolution, just like our own human DNA. Children who are delivered via caesarian section, or not breast feed will actually receive less of this inherited microbiome, and essential microbiota diversity, and the subsequent development of their immune and digestive system may even be adversely affected.[338]

To underscore the importance to humanity of this symbiotic holobiont relationship, the growth of our species may have been impossible without the invisible assistance of our fellow bionts. In breast milk, the natural and essential energy that it contains is locked within a complex carbohydrate called Human Milk Oligosaccharides (HMO).[339] These are naturally long chains of sugar molecules, sometimes bound with fats and proteins, that the body must break up into simpler compounds to be readily absorbed and utilised for energy and growth. They differ significantly from the carbohydrates present in almond, cow, or goat milk. The perplexing challenge, is that the human body does not naturally produce an enzyme that will break down the HMO's so that the infant can benefit from their nutrients. Thus, on the surface it may seem that feeding a baby breast milk will be suboptimal? In 2008, this puzzle was solved when a scientists sequenced a species of microbiota frequently present in breastfed infants called Bifidobacterium longum subsp. infantis (or B.Infantis).[340] It turns out that this particular microbiota is essential to human growth as, unlike humans, they posses an enzyme on their cell walls that effectively "snips" the bonds that holds the compounds of these HMO's together, liberating the component sugars, proteins, and fats to be easily absorbed by the growing baby.

Other strains of Bifidobacterium were tested to determine if they produced similar results, and this indicated that only B.Infantis had this unique effect.[341] It is suggested that this particular species of microbiota has evolved together with humanity to both feed off the HMO's in breast milk and, in the process, help support the growth and development of all people. The B.Infantis organism then patiently, passively, but purposively travels though time in partnership with humanity, as their genes are passed through breast milk from generation to generation helping us to grow, prosper, conquer and invent sliced bread. There are potentially even greater benefits to child rearing from the microbiome that are yet to be discovered. Research indicates that there is a species of microbiota that helps our body regulate the compound oxytocin, often regarded as the "love hormone" as it supports both social and reproductive behaviours. It promotes empathy and strengthens the bond between mother and child. Beyond this, oxytocin may even foster creativity in the human brain.[342] Therefore, a microbiota that helps humanity manage its most important developmental relationships and social connections may certainly have potential evolutionary benefits.

It is clear from the Human Microbiota Project that there is an immense amount of data to unpack on the multitude of roles and functions provided by the trillions of microbes that we share our bodies with. Their importance to nutrition, digestive heath, diseases of inflammation, and diabetes, are all being studied and are key to both wellness and development. What is also now emerging is the impact that the microbiota also has on our daily mental and emotional heath and the effect they may have on our decision-making ability and how we select ideas. The connection between our minds and intestines is commonly known as the "gut-brain" axis. What this describes is the direct connection between our central nervous system, which is the brain and spinal cord, and the enteric nervous system. This is the nerves that connect with the digestive tract. In other words, our brains do talk with our bowels.

Our busy microbiota can indirectly interact with and influence the enteric nervous system by producing incredible molecules that act as local neurotransmitters. These can be compounds such as serotonin, melatonin, histamine, or short chain fatty acids such as butyric acid.[343] The stimulation of the enteric neurones by these compounds, can have a direct impact on our central nervous system, brain function, and ultimately psychological well-being. A healthy microbiome is, therefore, important for overall physical and mental health, and balance. If the microbiome is deficient in a key regard, either due to environmental factors, poor diet, or an overuse of antibiotics, then the production of these molecules may be abnormally increased or suppressed. Ultimately, this can effect our wellbeing beyond general health and into psychological conditions such as anxiety and depression.[344]

Science is only just beginning to understand these connections, but one such condition being researched is autism in children. This, sometimes severe, affliction can have a significant short and long-term impact on social development. It can effect memory, learning abilities, reduce sociability, attention span, and increase frustration and anxiety. Research in both animals and in humans indicates that changes in a microbiome can positively reduce symptoms of autism.[345] For a period of time, physicians were anecdotally observing that there was a correlation between digestive health complaints, such as irritable bowl syndrome, together with the prevalence of conditions such as autism in children.[346] Additionally, records of over twenty million births identified that children delivered by caesarian section had a 33% higher chance as being diagnosed as autistic.[347] Further research also suggests another correlation as breast feeding decreases the risk of autism by 58%.[348] Of course, natural birth and breastfeeding are two important sources for hereditary microbiota. Although all these independent data points did not definitely prove casualty, they clearly pointed towards the negative impacts on child development from an absence of breastfeeding and natural birth, combined with digestive health complaints. This encouraged scientists to investigate this link further.

In studies dating back to 2014, research revealed that there was an increased chance of autism when there was a marked decrease in the levels of two particular amino acids that were actively produced in the digestive tract by a healthy microbiome. These amino acids were Five-aminovaleric acid, and taurine which are both positively correlated with healthy brain function. Following this research, a team from the University of Arizona selected eighteen children to receive a healthy increase in microbiota to assess any long-term impact from this change. The aim was to restore their microbiome balance and, in the process, increase the natural production of these essential amino acids to impact brain function. Over a four-month period they received doses of the healthy microbiota by either consuming capsules or via enemas. The scientists then monitored the children for signs of sustained improvement. Two years following this treatment, further tests were undertaken on the children to measure the changes in the degree of autism. Incredibly, results showed a decrease in the prevalence of autism in the group of over 47% compared to the control group.[349]

This provided strong evidence to suggest that the trillions of different species of organisms that happily inhabit our bodies can have a very subtle, but distinctive, impact on the brain function of developing children. How we perceive the world, how we interact with the world, and how we feel about our place in the world, may well be intertwined with retaining a healthy balance of these microbes. On a daily basis, we tend to ignore this connection, and for the most part, human civilisation didn't even know it existed. We do not consciously believe that our thoughts, emotions, and ideas may be directly influenced by chemical neurotransmitters, created by a vast universe of alien species of micro-organisms that live in their trillions in our colon, but it may well be the reality. If the microbiome is powerful enough to have a statistically significant impact on our cognitive abilities to increase the incidences of autism in children, and hamper our interaction with society, what other impacts can these organisms indirectly have on our everyday and critical decision-making ability? This is absolutely critical to the concept of idea selection and, therefore, the ability for our species to make the right choices.

When presented with internal or external ideas, humans need to make an active decision to ignore, follow, or reject them using our in-built mental algorithms. Research at Harvard University has identified a clear link between our emotional psychological state and the quality of our decision making ability. Their work reviewed over thirty-five years worth of independent scientific research and literature, and clearly supports the notion that our emotions constitute "powerful, pervasive, and predictable drivers of our decision making."[350] People who feel anxious, tend to make more risk-adverse decisions, and those that feel grateful tend to make more generous ones. Anger can lead people to make decisions that they perceive will enable them to take active control, while sadness can result in selecting a path that is passive and accepting fate.[351] Every person on the planet instinctively knows that emotions affect their decisions, and didn't really need Harvard to make this evident. Decisions made when we are angry, agitated, nervous, frustrated, or even in moments of intense passion have been ill-advised for centuries by everyone from priests to parents for very good reasons. Over two thousand years ago, the Roman philosopher, Lucius Annaeus Seneca the Younger, was already suggesting that bouts of intense anger were a form of temporary madness.[352]

The philosophic convention, is that when you are in a highly emotional state, our species has a track record of selecting sub-optimal ideas. So, to ensure that we make wise decisions or increase the possibility of selecting the best ideas, the human race is both scientifically, anecdotally, and philosophically advised to keep our emotions in balance. Easier said than done for many people, as reactions can be automatic and instinctive. What if the intensity of these emotions were partially triggered by the workings of an entirely separate species of microbiota living deep within us? How would we control them, or alternatively, are their biological interactions playing a passive, but secret part, in shaping how we make decisions?

There are many internal and external factors that influence our emotions, but new facts are emerging that indicate that the microbiota living and breeding within our bowels are impacting our psychology in measurable ways. In 2018, scientists from the University of Graz in Austria studied the effects in people consuming probiotics on emotional brain signatures after four weeks of consumption.[353] Probiotics are natural bacteria that can be safely consumed by humans which promote the healthy growth of species in the microbiome. These bacteria first need to survive the treacherous journey through the acidity of the stomach, traverse the twenty-two feet of the small intestines, to finally reach the microbiome living and growing in the lower intestine. Many perish along the way. Part of what makes this study so compelling is that the assessment of change was not only analysed on reported emotional states, but they used Magnetic Resonance Imaging (MRI) to peer inside the brain and obtain a visual map of any physical processing changes in the subjects taking the probiotics, compared to control groups, when given both emotional and memory-based tasks to complete.

The results indicated a win for the mighty microbiota. Subjects that were taking probiotics behaved significantly less risk-averse when making decisions and displayed less depression and vulnerability when measured on behavioural questionnaires.[354] Moreover, this was not just a perception from the subjects, as they recorded their feelings and judgements, it was mirrored in the MRI data as well. This revealed that their minds were now processing information very differently in areas of the brain traditionally involved in emotional decision-making and emotional memory processing. What this indicates is that the microbiome may be directly influencing what emotions we feel, and physically changing how the brain processes these emotions and ultimately, how we make decisions.

Imagine the consequences if the findings of this research could be broadly extrapolated across the general population. It's quite a leap, but may imply that people with a healthy microbiome intrinsically have increased confidence to make bolder choices for ideas, or readily accept fresher concepts. The people who's microbiome is deficient, impaired, or just different may be more cautious or timid in their choices and be less likely to risk entertaining a new idea. What would be the impact of this, when scaled across a society? Policies, politics, and even Presidents all promote and represent choices and ideas. Some ask people to embrace a bright future of new industries, new technology, and new forms of equality and diversity. Others rally for protectionism, supporting existing institutions, maintaining the status-quo while highlighting the risks of moving too fast or too soon. It is entirely possible that how an electorate responds to these ideas may be influenced, albeit in a small way, by the diversity and strength of the microscopic creatures living in their intestines and impacting their psychology.

This potential impact, first explored within autism, and now on decision making abilities, is still being researched, but is starting to reveal interesting insights across a range of other psychological and personality traits. Researchers at the University of Oxford in 2019, set about examining the correlations between the diversity of the microbiome and well-known human personality traits. Separate research had previously identified that, in animals, such as mice, personality traits could be exchanged across individuals by exchanging their microbiota. Species of mice that are known to be naturally timid and anxious, could suddenly behave like a completely different species of mice, more bold and exploratory, when the scientist clinically swapped their microbiota.[355] The reverse was also true. The species of bold mice would then become more timid.

To explore this concept in humans, researchers at Oxford University collected 655 individual fecal samples from healthy volunteers to analyse them for microbiota diversity, and then correlate that data with standardised personality questionnaires completed by the subjects.[356] The objective was to look for trends in personalities alongside the diversity and composition of microbiomes across the general population. After analysing the results, their conclusion was there is a clear link between personality traits such as sociability, anxiety, and openness with the diversity of the microbiome. All of these personality traits have an impact on our emotional state and how we react to external stimulus. The precise method of action, the quantum of change required in microbiota, and which of the 10,000 potential microbiota species has an impact, is still much less clear and needs further research, but the overall direction is gathering momentum. It appears that the microbiome can have an effect on our emotional state, brain function, and may have influence over how and why we make choices.

Humans are the dominant host, microbiomes are just the anonymous bionts, buried in our bowels, but it seems that their tails can truly wag our dog. The emotions, that you own and control, may be secretly nudged in various directions by the compounds released from a microscopic species living in your intestines. People do think with our guts in a very real sense. This 1kg universe of inner-species is constantly releasing compounds that impact how the human species engages and deals with the outside world and even what ideas we may choose to support or reject. Sustained diversity and balance in our microbiome is likely to have a meaningful degree of importance to our psychological wellbeing. What is also apparent is that there is individual variability in the composition of the microbiome. This is driven by a number of factors, including initial inheritance, diet, sociability, travel, and engagement with nature.[357]

Unfortunately, in parallel with this growing understanding, there is arguably a growing global mental health crisis with recent data indicating that almost one in ten people suffer from some from of mental disorder, and over 540 million people worldwide reportedly live with either depression, or an anxiety disorder.[358] It is impossible to say how much of this is connected with or could be assisted by, changes in the microbiome, except to state that there is a body of evidence that implies improvements in microbiome may help solve this imbalance, for at least some individuals.

The overuse of antibiotics is one area that has a significant impact on the composition of a person's microbiome. This is because the antibiotic is engineered to kill microbes, and quite often, indiscriminately so. Therefore, whilst they may be deployed to fight a specific infection, they may also be carpet-bombing the good bacteria that lives within us and significantly reduce the diversity of our microbiome during the course of the medication.[359] This balance usually rebounds within six months, but prolonged usage of antibiotics can create other complications such as diabetes and asthma.[360] What negative impact on brain function that may also occur during this period is unknown, but what is problematic is that the use of antibiotics around the world is growing significantly.

Although usage has plateaued in a number of western markets, much of the world is still accelerating in application, and prescription of antibiotics. A recent meta-data analysis gathered statistics from seventy-six countries between 2000 and 2015. It estimated that the consumption of antibiotics in these countries increased by a staggering 65% from twenty-one billion daily doses in 2000, to nearly thirty-five billion in 2015.[361] The USA still leads the way with approximately 270 million antibiotic prescriptions issued in 2015. This amounts to an incredible 838 antibiotic prescriptions for every 1,000 Americans, every year.[362] While these antibiotics undoubtably save countless lives, they are also becoming less effective, as microbes build a resistance to them. The potential impact they have on psychological and brain function from unintended damage to the microbiome is largely left unmeasured and ignored. However, it may be indirectly impacting our psychological approach when selecting the best ideas to improve our daily lives.

Some leading microbiome scientists, such as Susan Erdman, a principal research scientist and assistant director of MIT's Division of Comparative Medicine, argues that our microbiome could be important enough to help advance human evolution itself.[363] She cites the growing body of research that highlights the symbiotic relationship that humans have with our bionts to assist with a wide assortment of improvements in health, nutrition, growth, disease reduction, and developmental needs. Early stage research shows that while there are similarities between the human microbiome when compared to our closest primates, there are unique differences as well. In fact, humans, on average, show higher levels for eleven microbial species and lower levels in twenty others, when compared to most other apes and monkeys.[364] It is highly probable that as our species took the bold steps to migrate to new geographies, explore new climates and environments, and in the process, consumed widely diversified food choices as a social omnivore. This may have enriched our ancestors' microbiome significantly over time.[365]

Importantly, for the future health of our population, there is evidence to indicate that the microbiome from humans living in an agricultural setting is more diverse and robust, than those living in an urban setting, where they are more likely to be eating highly processed foods, are less in touch with nature, and live in more sterile environments.[366] This signifies a warning to the continued trajectory of global mental health. Given that for the first time in human history, people now predominantly live in urban environments,[367] combined with the accelerated use of antibiotics, sanitisers, the consumption of highly processed foods, and caesarean births reaching 32% in western countries[368], our microbiome may now be at risk of degenerating in quality across the population. How this might impact our mental health and our collective evolution and progress as a species is unclear.

Perhaps science has only scratched the surface of our evolved interdependence with this microscopic ecosystem. If the degradation of a specific species of microbiota can measurably, and negatively, impact our cognitive abilities to such an extent that it increases the probability of autism, could the reverse also be true? Are there unidentified species of microbiota that could have a more positive role in our brain function, if cultivated in abundance within our colon? If characteristics of risk adverse, openness, sociability and anxiety can be impacted by our bionts, can creativity, imagination, and lateral thinking be maximised by direct intervention of our microbiome? Could the history of the evolving ideas of mankind be somehow linked to the co-evolution of the many species that feed and breed in our microbiome? Without them continually creating compounds, that interact with our nervous system, would we have had the edge in cognitive abilities or convictions to make the creative leaps forward, or the optimal brain functions to select the right ideas when balancing risk adversity with curiosity and ingenuity?

For example, science already knows that creativity correlates with the presence of the hormone oxytocin in brain functions.[369] Why this may be powerfully relevant is that, separately, science has also identified that a particular species of microbiota, Lactobacillus reuteri, assists the human body by up-regulating our response to oxytocin. This implies that humans are sensitive to the impact of oxytocin regulated by our microbiome, which in turn stimulates our creative pathways.[370] Microbiota, living within our colon, could have had an evolutionary impact on the expansion of human creativity and the generation of new ideas, by quietly helping to up-regulate the natural hormones that have enhanced both our longevity and ingenuity across thousands of years. A better neural-chemical process for managing oxytocin could increase the probability of survival through creativity, and may plausibly be amplified by evolution over generations via the mechanism of natural selection. These unique microbiota would also be highly likely to be inherited from generation to generation, thereby increasing the potential impact they may play on our species' successful evolution.

What is deeply concerning, is that, particularly in the western world, we are creating a perfect storm against the microbiome. The combined elements of aggressive antibiotic use, over-processed food consumption, and unparalleled urbanisation shown to deplete our microbiome, which otherwise would strengthen our immune systems and influence our nervous systems to a measurable level. This may eventually negatively affect important psychological brain functions, raise the level of mental disorders, increase inflammatory diseases, and impair decision making at a time when technology, information, and ideas are exploding both in terms of pace and quantum. Critically, all this may be converging when the pressure of getting idea selection decisively right is very high and the dire consequences of getting it wrong have never been greater for our communities.

Sadly, the developing world is following the exact path on urbanisation, antibiotic use, and processed food consumption as the western world. If there ever was truly a time in history where we needed a close partnership with the microscopic species that makes up our beautifully evolved microbiome, it is now. Arguably, we are, however, passively engineering a society that promotes the very opposite, partly in ignorance and partly from hubris. Believing we are a dominant solo species, when we are actually a holobiont, is an illusion of scale. Perhaps our species didn't conquer the planet, split the atom, and write Bohemian Rhapsody totally alone. Microbiota are an essential evolutionary partner to the human race that should never be taken for granted. They have uniquely helped our growth, wellness, mental heath and creativity. We must nurture them so we can be at a peak mental condition to chart the ideas that will determine our future. Although, they may not be the only essential evolutionary symbiotic relationship that we will ever have and need to partner with. There may well be new ones lurking just over the horizon.

CHAPTER 11

THE AUGMENTED APE.

Around 3,000 BC, the ancient civilisation of Sumer had thriving industries energetically trading grains, wool, dates, oils, figs, metals, animals, and many other valuable commodities.[371] These transactions occurred not just between their key city states of Eridu, Uruk, and Larsa, but across the Iranian peninsula into Egypt and well beyond. Items like cedar trees from distant Lebanon were imported for their strength in construction. In this brimming and vibrant emerging economy, there were thousands of people buying, selling, and paying taxes on thousands of different items. They needed new ideas to help them reduce friction in the system and keep their world operating smoothly. One such essential idea was money. This originally emerged across the region as silver rings or clay tokens, often stamped with symbolic icons. These were received by labourers and could then be directly exchanged for wheat, honey, oils, or even beer. The Sumerians then had a brand new idea that would eventually become a global breakthrough. They created a bronze coin as a new symbol of value. This was designed to allow access to the Temple of Ishtar. If a citizen of Sumer wanted to pray for a healthy crop, a growing family, or other gifts from the divine, they needed to seek blessing from Ishtar, The Goddess of Fertility. A bushel of wheat was deemed by the Gods to be the minimum appropriate offering. A bushel was approximately 3.6kg or the roughly the amount of wheat a Sumerian could comfortably squeeze into a bucket. Once this was reverently passed to the Temple Priests, the citizen would then receive a bronze coin called a "shekel", stamped with the symbols for both wheat and the mighty Ishtar herself.

This coin was now an idea. It represented a symbolic unit of measurement for the weight of a bushel. Freshly armed with the shekel, the blessed visitor could immediately exchange it for an afternoon with the sacred prostitutes of the Temple to receive the fertile fruits of their blessing in the flesh.[372] Over time, the shekel expanded beyond the core necessity of spending quality "alone-time" with the earthly representatives of Ishtar, to eventually spawn into a medium of exchange for many other items such as food, clothing, labour, and even fines, taxes, or even a new slave. All forms of money on the planet today potentially owes its origins to the strangely pious beginnings of that humble bronze shekel.

Booming trade and population growth, when combined with this revolutionary idea of money, triggered a secondary problem for the Sumerians, how to keep track of it all. They were facing the same problem that every high-school student in a mathematics exam has nervously encountered. Mental additional and subtraction is often vexing with the limited computing power we all genetically carry in our skulls. The Sumerians calculated everything in their world based on a sexagesimal system, or what is known as "base 60".[373] It is widely believed that this naturally emerged from their cultural habit of counting to sixty with their fingers. The method involved counting to twelve on their right hand by tapping the thumb at each of the three segments on each of the four fingers of that hand. When they reached twelve, they would raise a finger on their left hand. When all five fingers of the left hand were raised, they had then reached the magic sixty.

A simple enough system, that has subsequently had a seismic cultural impact on humanity over the last 5,000 years. Although the world has long-since shifted to the Arabic system of "base 10", many of the operating systems of modern daily life still champion the innovative echoes of this early Sumerian sexagesimal system. There are sixty seconds in a minute, sixty minutes in an hour, a single day is two times twelve hours, twelve months in a year, and our entire planet is divided into 360 degrees, and twenty-four time zones. All of this is in base sixty and can be loosely traced to the long-deceased tapping fingers of the entrepreneurial Sumerians.[374] They had already invented a system of writing on clay tablets to record their daily transactions, but now they required additional help to augment their biological hardware. They needed new ideas to deal with the growing complexity of computations that were filling their economies, cities, lives, and minds. In around 2,700 BC, they invented one, that would slowly ripple through time and change all civilisation. The world's first abacus or "counting board", that leveraged their cultural methodology of counting on base sixty. It was a flat clay tablet, designed with grooves, where tokens could be placed to represent specific values. Place a token along the first two grooves, and amounts up to sixty were tabulated that mirrored their "finger-tapping" methodology. Placing a single token in the third groove would then immediately represent sixty itself. One token in the next subsequent groove could then represent 600, then 6,000, and so forth. In one leap, large sums could be tabulated quickly and added or subtracted with unparalleled efficiency and unequivocal transparency. In effect, they had created the world's first computational device, or what we now call, a computer. To illustrate how far ahead of their time they were, while the innovative Sumerians were busily calculating on their counting boards, the tax rate on shipments of fresh figs at their warm freshwater ports on the banks of the Euphrates river, a tranquil herd of Woolly Mammoths, that had survived the end of the ice age, were still quietly grazing in Siberia.[375]

Another relentless domino fell in Sumer the day they innocently, but ingeniously, conceived their idea of the counting board. Humanity simultaneously exposed the vulnerable intersection between a soft underbelly and a great strength. The world the Sumerians had created had become too complex for the human mind to easily keep pace with. The brain had evolved over millennia to deal with the mathematics of a natural world, not necessarily an economic one. Their brains searched for the crutch of outside assistance to augment its capabilities, to keep on top of the frenetic new reality that their intellects had created. Luckily, the human mind had the ability to invent new technology that could allow it to keep up with their economic world. In the early days in Sumer, our species realised that we needed to outsource a degree of intellectual responsibility to ideas like a counting board. These devices could bridge the gap between the world we had civilised, and the computational limits of our biological minds. The double-edged sword was that on a long-term basis, the more we developed the complexity of the economic and materialist world, the smarter the technology that we would need to support our minds so we could continue to thrive in it.

Humanity was in no immediate rush to try and balance this equation, as the evolution of these counting boards was far from exponential. The Greeks, Romans, and Chinese eventually all had their own variations of the counting board that they utilised from approximately 500 BC onwards. Between that period and the Middle Ages (5th to 15th Century AD), history records that only relatively slow, but deliberate, improvements to the basic structure of the abacus were made. Primarily to allow them to handle slightly more sophisticated computations, and to allow for ease of transportation.

The only major outlier to this apparent linear development in computational power is the "Antikythera mechanism" named after being discovered in an ancient shipwreck off the coast of a picturesque Greek island, which bears the same name. Rescued from the seabed in 1901, it is a verified anomaly dating back to between 200 and 87 BC. It is a hand-powdered computer, designed to calculate, among other things, the lunar cycle across an astounding 19-year time span, together with the corresponding movement of planets and even constellations. It is immensely sophisticated, and incredibly impressive with at least thirty bronze mechanical cogs interconnected to perform the required calculations.[376] While there is documented evidence that around the same time the legendary Greek inventor, Archimedes, was indeed developing sophisticated mechanisms to study the movement of planets and stars[377], no analogous contemporaneous technology has ever been discovered, and no precursors or prototypes have been unearthed. Whoever held the precious knowledge and skills to create such advanced counting mechanisms, took it to their graves. The idea of using a sophisticated system of engineering to track time did not re-emerge until the 5th Century AD in the middle-east, and even later still in Europe, with the creation of mechanical clocks in the late 13th century AD.[378]

Since then, humanity has picked up the pace a little on developing ideas to increase computing power, and in the process, augment our inherent biological abilities. One of the catalysts for the acceleration, was to conquer a problem similar to that faced by the Sumerians; tabulating exponentially growing numbers. In 1880, the population of the US had already reached fifty million people and was presenting the US Census with a significant challenge. It was taking an unmanageable seven years to manually process all of the data that was received by the census survey.[379] The limitations of manual human computation were exposed as inefficient and inadequate for the monumental task required by the growing nation. The US Census needed a much faster idea. This was provided by their former employee, Herman Hollerith, who leveraged the ingenuity of an automatic weaving machine, the Jacquard Loom. In this machine, intricate designs were informed by sets of coded punch cards.

Hollerith's insight was that the position of the holes on the punch cards could potentially complete an electric circuit, and thus, register binary information which would enable the rapid categorisation and tabulation of any massive and complex data set, at a vastly increased pace, relative to the laborious manual methodology. First demonstrated to the US Census in 1887, he quickly secured a contract with them for the 1890 census, and shortly after this initial proven success he secured lucrative contracts with the Governments of Norway, Canada and Austria. Under the banner of his new enterprise, the "Tabulating Machine Company" he quickly increased his prices to leverage better profits.[380]

By 1910, the US Census had decided to develop their own tabulating machines in response to the soaring monopolistic prices requested by Hollerith. The Tabulating Machine Company was then subsequently merged with three other strategically similar businesses, producing weighing machines and punch-time clocks. This combined company was then rebranded as the Computer Tabulating Recording Company.[381] By this time, Herman Hollerith was progressively taking a step back from daily management, and Thomas J. Watson Senior joined the company in 1914 as General Manager and was subsequently promoted to President in 1915. By 1924, he had refocussed and renamed the company "International Business Machines", or what the world knows today as the computing powerhouse, IBM.[382] By 2019, IBM had amassed over 350,000 employees generating US$77 billion in revenue.[383] This significant scale had taken over 4,500 years to build since the invention of the Sumerian counting board, but the bright spark of the next revolution in information processing had finally occurred. It was ignited by the growing complexity of the industrial world, designed to bridge the growing gap between the limits of people's biological computational power and the economic advances in human ingenuity.

This necessity to innovate in computational power, paved the way for true ground-breakers of computing such as Alan Turing, Gordon Welchman, Harry Huskey, and other pioneers who all made incredible advances in the field during the 1930s and 40s. These pioneers even broke the codes that helped to defeat the Nazis and save lives, creating peace.[384] The Nazi's themselves were horrendous early adopters when it came to computing. As early as 1933, they were reportedly using IBM punch-card tabulating technology to collect broad national census data, partly to identify the German-Jewish population, so they could precisely define their numbers, location, and relatives.[385] Even more sickening, is the documented reports that many of the most horrific Nazi death camps insanely and brutally utilised electronic tabulators to keep definitive track of deaths, suicides, executions, and genocide on these flimsy punch-cards, calmly coded by teams of Nazi sociopaths.[386]

After America joined World War II, it became fully engaged in a race to develop technology and tools to help them drive to victory and defeat the expansion plans of the Nazis and Axis powers. One of the earliest, programable digital computers, was commissioned during the war in 1943, but remained top-secret until publicly revealed in 1946. Called the Electronic Numerical Integrator and Computer, or ENIAC, it can still be seen at the Smithsonian today.[387] It was conceived and constructed at the University of Pennsylvania by Professors John Mauchly and J. Presper Eckert. Importantly, the complex and vital task of programming ENIAC was entrusted to six resilient and brilliant young women. As war raged across the world, and many educated men were serving in the Armed Forces, professors entrusted the operation of ENIAC to an all-female crew of graduate mathematicians that may have otherwise been overlooked for all the wrong reasons. These pioneers were Fran Bilas, Betty Jennings, Ruth Lichterman, Kay McNulty, Betty Snyder, and Marlyn Wescoff.[388] Without them, the operation of ENIAC and the advancement of computing, may not have been possible.

Just as DNA is passed from generation to generation, ENIAC inherited the IBM punch card technology to both input and export data. This harked all the way back to the original 1887 innovation by Hollerith. The total machine weighed about the same as fifteen Ford trucks, and laid out straight, it would have been 8ft high and almost as long as a basketball court. It could crunch at least 5,000 calculations per second which it squeezed through 18,000 sizzling vacuum tubes, 70,000 resistors, 10,000 capacitors, 6,000 switches, and 1,500 relays.[389] It was a counting board of truly biblical proportions. Although hailed as a monumental advancement in science at the time, its power was relatively impotent by today's immense computing capabilities. The intent of ENIAC was a little more sinister, however. The world's first-ever digital computer was secretly commissioned and paid for by the US Army during the final years of World War II. ENIAC's first tasks were to complete the necessary calculations to help construct a hydrogen bomb[390] and execute complicated artillery range calculus calculations, to enable long-range ammunition to be rapidly effective. What would have taken a human twelve hours to complete, the ENIAC could now spit out on a crisp IBM style punchcard in just thirty seconds.[391] It was a true milestone in technological advancement, but the founding idea was to give the US Army a strategic advantage in battle, by killing more efficiently.

The potential commercial value of ENIAC was significant and, almost predictably, there was a corresponding battle of glutinous greed over ownership of the idea. Despite starting the project in 1943 and publicly announcing it in 1946, Mauchly and Eckert did not formally submit a US patent application until 1947. By then, who owned the intellectual property or the idea of ENIAC, was not entirely clear. Professors Mauchly and Eckert had previously collaborated with another leading US mathematician, John von Neumann. He had circulated a separate paper in 1945 which canvassed similar territory as the ENIAC innovation and this caused further complications in assigning intellectual ownership.[392]

Neumann, by all accounts, was a truly gifted mathematical genius, and his ideas were simultaneously groundbreaking, inspiring, deathly, and potentially planet-saving. During the 1940s he was an instrumental figure in the Manhattan Project that was tasked with secretly developing the atomic bomb to help end the fascist horror of World War II. His ideas and calculations were an essential part for optimising atomic detonation, as well as contributing to the devilish insight that, if a bomb was triggered 1,700 ft above the ground, the blast impact and killing power, would be significantly improved.[393] He was also a part of the team that helped select the atomic targets of Hiroshima and Nagasaki and, as a result, may have been intimately involved in discussing the deaths of thousands of civilians and numerous strategic targets.[394]

One of the candidate Japanese cities under consideration for nuclear destruction, was Kyoto, not only for military reasons, but also because it was the home to a number of important Universities. The reported argument, from a number of the Manhattan Project scientists, was that, if an atomic bomb vaporised the intellectual community of these Universities, it would simultaneously obliterate their ideas from the face of the Earth. This act would have crippled Japan's ability to develop retaliatory weapons for decades and was part of a defensive strategy.[395] Scientists targeting to massacre scientists, to eliminate the other scientist's future ideas. Now, that's an idea only a human mind could conceive.

Neumann was also a leading expert on game theory. He was one of the first within the intelligence community to raise the alarm over the emerging threat that the Soviets would soon assemble the ability to launch massive nuclear attacks against the USA. He is often credited with the brazen idea of "Mutually Assured Destruction" (MAD) which was the decisively delicate, but also deliberately dangerous, balance of overwhelming nuclear weaponry by opposing forces, so that no individual party would gain an advantage by pulling the atomic trigger.[396] Perhaps supported by this theory, he was apparently one of the stronger voices that pushed the US Government to accelerate the atomic arms race, which eventually resulted in the tense and fierce equilibrium of the Cold War. The Americans and the Russians were like two titanic bulls, facing each other on a tightrope, strung high over a field of radioactive landmines, in a hurricane. Constant bluff and patience was the only smart play.

If Neumann hadn't passionately believed in this idea, and the Soviets were allowed to build vastly superior nuclear capability, unchecked by American innovation, perhaps the Western world would have been reduced to nothing more than a smouldering pile of radioactive ashes during the bold communist expansion of the 1960s. Nuclear war was a very present and probable reality in the decades following World War II. Perhaps the fact that human civilisation survived through this period, relatively unscathed, may mean that we owe our existence to Neumann's ideas on the power of military brinkmanship. Or perhaps we survived in spite of his MAD idea? There may have been many better paths available that our leaders simply did not take?

Regarding the important ENIAC patents, the US Courts continued to wrestle over them all the way to 1973, when it was eventually declared that the original 1945 "John von Neumann paper" was deemed to be prior-art and that the idea of ENIAC could not sit with Professors Mauchly and Eckert.[397] Unfortunately, Neumann did not live to see this decision. He died of cancer some sixteen years earlier in 1957, at the young age of just 53, but not before leaving a substantial mark on the evolution of human ideas.

Despite the legal challenges for the originality of their ideas, and emboldened by their entrepreneurial flame, Professors Mauchly and Eckert knew that their future ideas could still be monetised, and were determined not to make the same mistakes again. In 1947, they left their positions at the University of Pennsylvania and formed their own business, The Electronic Control Company[398] focussed on developing new innovations in processing power, above and beyond ENIAC. Over the following decades, and through multiple mergers and acquisitions, their pioneering company eventually became part of the major industrial technology leader we now know today as Unisys.[399] A global computing company with over 21,000 employees and nearly US$ 3 billion in revenue.[400]

It had taken humanity many millennia to slowly evolve our tabulating ideas beyond the soft clay genesis of the Sumerian abacus. After Herman Hollerith profited from his paper punchcards, designed to rapidly sort the lives of US citizens, it wasn't long before humans began to eagerly delegate many of the complex calculations necessary to potentially eradicate the lives of thousands, if not millions, to artificial and augmented ideas, created to optimise the things we freshly engineered, such as conventional and nuclear war.

Although the US Army commissioned ENIAC, the artillery calculations arrived too late for World War II. However, the idea of using computing power to shortcut the process of perfecting a kill strike was perhaps the dirty precursor of every smart bomb, predator drone, and guided missile that has bombarded soldiers, civilians, ships, and cities ever since. In that context, which civilisation is using data-driven ideas for a more moral and civilised purpose? The sun-drenched Sumerian merchant, using clay tablets to count their trade of wheat, beer, and slaves? Or modern society, delegating silicon circuits to segment, target, and eradicate people more efficiently via the sanitised remote use of predator drones? Since the pivotal moment when the power switch to the ENIAC was flicked on, augmenting the mental processing capabilities of the human race through external technological ideas, has exponentially accelerated and expanded. Arguably, so have the systemic risks and benefits to society from these same ideas, especially if we lose control of how and where these ideas operate.

Today, we could consider at least 45% of the planet is partly augmented, as global smartphone penetration, and, therefore, the percentage of people who have fingertip-access to the internet, has reached this level.[401] This provides people with abilities way beyond mere tabulations, and instantly supplements unlimited data to almost any question, or challenge presented. This has been driven by the plummeting costs of computing power and data transmission, combined with the increased efficiencies of transistors, predicted by Moores Law, the co-founder of the computer processor giant, Intel. This states that the number of transistors on a circuit will double every two years.[402] Since 1975, this Law has held straight and true, and in the process, has delivered powerful and affordable computing power into the hands of over 3 billion people. For a millennium, humanity has searched their minds and memories to recall facts and information. Now the computing and associated digital transformation industry is a trillion-dollar economy that enables any person, augmented with this technology, to bypass and supplement their biological computation power and genetic memory banks with superior silicon-based search, storage, and emerging intelligent computational systems.

The reality is that, like our biological ecosystems, artificially augmenting our intelligence has been constantly evolving and slowly cocooning humans since we first scratched red-ochre symbols onto cave walls. This technological augmentation has been relentlessly inching forward throughout civilisations, as the people within them rise and fall. It has not been powered by Darwin's genetic evolution, where our genes hold the advantages for the next generation. Instead, it has been driven by the separate mechanism of idea evolution. Humanity passes on creative and lateral breakthroughs across generations, so each new cohort innovates upon the ideas of their ancestors. Although this relay race of ideas has been running for over 7,500 human generations, what has dramatically changed in almost the span of a single generation is that the volume, the pace, the power, and the consequences of our ideas. They are now exponentially more powerful, pervasive, beautiful, and destructive than ever before. For the first time in the history of the planet, survival of the fittest may now be determined by how we manage our fast-moving and impactful ideas, more than the relatively slow-paced mechanism of our genes.

Some may argue that technological augmentation is a very improbable futuristic scenario, and humans won't fully supplement their abilities with technology. However, augmentation of human capabilities is already widespread and seeping into many facets of everyday life. Approximately 59% of the global population already has daily access to the internet[403] to supplement both short and long-term memory. It assists with tasks and computations such as tracking fitness, trading stocks, solving problems, connecting with friends or family, and a million other ways to create, relax, waste time, share angst, or hoard wealth.

In the financial sector, it is estimated that at least 50% of all trades on the NASDAQ are already conducted by what is known as "High-Frequency Trading" algorithms, making decisions to buy and sell shares in companies, at speeds measured in microseconds.[404] So rapid that no vast army of pin-striped, Armani suited, MBA analysts could ever compete with. Other industries which rely on market-based pricing have also handed the keys to these types of algorithms. Sectors such as the global travel industry prefer the profits that yield from silicon circuits rather than from people when setting their prices. This industry leverages dynamic algorithms to adjust the pricing of a plane ticket to Prague or a hotel in the Hamptons based on predicted demand, customer profiles, routes, and algorithms designed to anticipate how desperate you might be for a seat to urgently reach a meeting, a wedding, or a funeral.[405] When it comes to augmenting human abilities in other industries, technologies dependent on algorithms have been designed with what is called narrow artificial intelligence (AI).[406] This means that they can be excellent at completing a very specific task, or defined function only. For example, in the medical health sector, algorithms are now regularly outperforming trained radiologists at analysing and reading mammograms, to identify high-risk cancer lesions in patients that may need surgery.[407]

The legal profession is also no exception. In the USA, narrow AI systems have been employed to streamline tasks such as court filings, document management, and even risk assessment of defendants. True, they do sometimes make mistakes, and the algorithms utilised can have appalling social and racial biases, but despite this, they are being actively utilised and will undoubtedly be refined over time. For example, in the Los Angeles Superior Court, they have employed "Gina", an AI-powered online avatar, to handle the mountain of traffic citations. Since being launched in 2016, Gina handles 550 transactions a day and has reduced court wait times dramatically.[408]

Globally, farmers are also increasingly using narrow AI systems to create seasonal crop forecasting models and improve agricultural precision and increase productivity. These programs are engineered to predict local weather patterns, to assist the decisions of farmers on what crops to plant or when to harvest to maximise yield.[409] Whether it is our private, social, professional, fitness, health, media, social or consumer lives there is probably an algorithm silently and slyly spinning in the background, either augmenting our decisions or, at the very least, managing the options that are presented to us. We are progressively and passively becoming a civilisation augmented by technology and slowly passing over our control of options and decisions to evolving forms of AI. It is predicted to only accelerate from this already frenetic point.

One of the most visible and publicly debated areas of augmentation, is the rapidly emerging industry of autonomous driving. Most major automotive brands, ride-hauling companies, and many technology companies, such as Apple and Google, all either have a strategy, or a product, which is accelerating in this space and racing for dominance. If there is an industry where humans may urgently need assistance, it is certainly this one. Globally, there is an average of 1.35 million deaths in automobile accidents, and up to fifty million significant injuries every year. Sadly, road injuries are also the global leading cause of death for children above five years of age.[410] In the USA, the risk of dying from a car crash is one in 114, whereas the equivalent risk in an aeroplane, where there is already a higher degree of automation, is only one in 9,821.[411] Many of the most devastating road accidents are due to human error. In Germany, in a single year, there were 300,000 accidents resulting in injuries, and research has shown that up to 90% of them were linked to human error.[412] Economically and morally, humanity should desperately seek the help of algorithms to stamp on the brakes of this problem, that our brains are apparently not able to solve and, are more often than not, the cause.

The Tesla Autopilot system already claims to make the roads a safer place. They calculate that their system will, on average, have only one accident per 4.34 million miles, up to nine times safer than human drivers.[413] In theory, the wide-scale adoption of fully-tested automated driving could save millions of injuries and thousands of lives. Elon Musk, the Innovator and CEO of Tesla, believes it is quickly becoming a reality. He recently shared with investors that "It's almost getting to a point where I can go from my house to work with no interventions, despite going through construction and widely varying situations. So this is why I'm very confident about its full self-driving functionality being complete by the end of this year. It's because I'm literally driving it."[414] There is no doubt that the idea of progressively automating transport into a synchronised harmony of mobile-precision, will eventually save lives. How quickly this occurs will depend on many legal and industrial factors, but one of them may be related to our ideas on the morality of the technological solution, and whether the automated driving algorithms will share the same values as the humans they eventually share the roads with.

This issue revolves around a series of improbable, yet certainly possible, decisions that an autonomous driving AI may be faced with and will need to adjudicate on. For example, a travelling car may be instantly faced with a certain impending crash that there is no escaping from. The only choices of impact are to either swerve left into a wall, killing the driver, to mount the footpath and kill a child walking home, or continue straight and kill the passengers in the oncoming car. What should the autonomous driving AI decide to do in this scenario? What would a human driver do? Will all cars behave the same, or will some brands be programmed and marketed to protect the owner of the car over innocent pedestrians on the pavement or visa versa? Which is the best of these obviously bad scenarios and ideas?

It turns out, that everyday human motorists are conflicted with their answers to these challenges. They often state one answer, if they simply consider themselves to be an observer to the accident, and then a completely different one, if they assume they are the parent to the child at risk, or the passenger in the soon-to-be mangled steel coffin that the algorithm may actively select to be killed. The morality of the idea is often completely fluid depending on where the person sits in the scenario, and what skin they have in the game.[415]

As part of an expansive social experiment to crowd-source solutions for this challenge, The Massachusetts Institute of Technology created an online survey called "The Moral Machine"[416] aimed at collecting global answers to a range of these life or death traffic predicaments. Crunching the numbers, from over 2.3 million responses in 233 countries to thirteen different challenges, revealed many religious and geographic differences. Unfortunately, it also revealed no unifying morality of ideas to guide an AI system. People in western countries were less likely to favour ideas that saved the lives of young people or women. Asia was more inclined to spare lawful citizens and innocent pedestrians. While some countries exhibited significant economic inequalities, like Columbia, where more were willing to select a poor person to be eliminated by an oncoming car than a rich person.[417]

What this research highlighted are the endlessly complex mental algorithms that humans have developed to select ideas, and how they are highly dependent on each person's individual experiences and beliefs. It is these unique factors that ensure that everyone's calculations end up being completely subjective decisions. When it comes to moral choices of selecting who should survive and who should die, humanity is not able to speak with one voice or one shared universal idea. There will be a natural spread of often-conflicting ideas, created and selected by people. This makes it almost impossible for even the most ingenious narrow AI to completely mirror how a human may make decisions while driving a car, as humans are often endlessly subjective and not transparently objective.

Despite this, there will undoubtedly emerge a truly automated driving solution, and there will eventually be cars with completely autonomous driving AI. It is also very likely that as the populations of autonomous roads grow, the safer our roads will become, as the often deadly idiosyncrasies of humans will be progressively removed. However, they will not be simply replacing human decision making, but in many ways, elevating it, by improving upon human consistency, or deliberately not replicating inherently subjective biases. A consequence of this upgrade, is that humans may ultimately need to delegate instantaneous life and death choices on both passengers and pedestrians, to the narrow

AI embedded in their cars. Human decisions may not be an accurate, predictable, or objective enough system to be exactly replicated by our rapidly developing technology.

If society wants to make a dramatic and rapid impact on reducing 1.35 million road deaths a year, we will need an intelligent system devoid of the inherent flaws of people. Estimates from the US Department of Transport suggest that fully embracing automation would reduce deaths by up to 94%.[418] To achieve these levels, a massive proportion of all cars would need to automated and road quality would also need to be maintained, if not significantly improved. All of these evolving and self-learning financial, medical, industrial, public, and lifestyle augmentations, designed to surpass our inherent biological limitations, are external to the human body, connected to separate infrastructure and poorly integrated with our biology or cognitive decision-making abilities. Another evolution of AI development will be to integrate new intelligent technologies directly with our minds, our senses, or nervous systems.

The initial objectives may be to repair biological damages, an important innovation that will restore mobility, cognition, sight and independence to millions of people. Eventually, they will also be used to enhance people, both physically and mentally, to ensure that our species doesn't become outmoded and replaced by the very artificial ideas we are now creating. This is not science fiction, but current research and investment by a number of the leading billionaires on the planet. Their conclusion seems to be that the next stage of human evolution does not have the patience to wait for the painstakingly slow relay-race of random mutations, passing genetic batons across multiple generations to ultimately reveal the majesty of their improvements. Instead, the significant investment in integrating AI with our biology is aimed squarely at making humans instantly fitter for survival. The pace of this development is very likely to leave traditional evolution rapidly, decisively, and even permanently in its wake. Improvements to humanity may now be driven and measured more by integrating silicon than carbon-based DNA.

The poster-child for this next stage of idea development is Elon Musk, the entrepreneur seemingly so smart, he makes even some of his iconic contemporaries sound as insightful as late-night infomercials. In 2016, he launched Neuralink, his next world-changing company. Their stated goal is to "create the future of brain interfaces by building devices that will help people with paralysis, and inventing new technologies that will expand our abilities, our community, and our world."[419] In other words, Neuralink's plan seems to be to create technology that helps make humanity smarter, faster, stronger, and better fit for long-term prosperity. This sounds exactly like what Darwin suggested that our genetic evolution was busily doing for the past few billion years, only now quicker and funded by capital.

Neuralink's nascent Brain-Machine Interface (BMI) is still in its early stages, but they have publicly showcased trials in pigs, which successfully demonstrates that they can integrate their implanted neural computer chips directly with the electrical signals of a brain. They have also implanted wireless chips into the brains of monkeys, which is currently assisting them to control video games with their minds.[420] As a parallel development, the surgery required to connect the thousands of wires to transfer data from the brain to the Neuralink device isn't handled by the fiddly fingers of human doctors. To increase precision, speed, and minimise the risk, they have developed a bespoke eight-foot surgical robot to perform the augmentation operation.[421] Neuralink is, therefore, designing robots to help merge mankind with technology. The immediate goals of Neuralink are to help people with paralysis regain independence through the control of computers, to give people the ability to communicate easier via text or speech synthesis, to follow their curiosity on the web, and to express their creativity through photography, art, or writing.[422] This is the strategic equivalent of integrating the computing power, speed and, internet access of a smartphone directly into the intricate synaptic pathways of the brain. This simply cuts out the relatively clunky and clumsy current interfaces of fingers, ears, and eyes. The resulting metamorphosis in human potential may be spectacular.

Exactly where the BMI technology is at today is not as relevant as to where the entire category will be in ten, twenty, or a hundred years into the future. Neuralink may or may not grow to be widely successful and dominate the sector but some company will. In either case, the quantum of investment, range of ideas, and pace of innovation in the BMI industry won't abate, and in all probability, will have a significant impact on humanity.

Facebook has also started exploring this space with a 2019 investment in a company called CRTL-Labs[423] who's nascent technology is less evasive. They are currently producing a wristband capable of transmitting electrical signals from the brain into a computer. The ambition, however, is much broader as Mark Zuckerberg, Facebook Founder and CEO, stated that their goal is to "eventually make it so that you can think something and control something in virtual or augmented reality."[424] To that end, Facebook also funds several research programs in this space. One such study was at the University of California, designed to fine-tune the accuracy of decoding human speech from brain signals alone. The algorithms could translate human speech from just the electronic neural activity measured in the brain to an accuracy of 97%.[425] Therefore, as you think the words, the computer reads your mind. A form of digital telepathy is just around the corner and will revolutionise how ideas are formed, and how they are communicated and shared.

A division of Facebook, highly focussed on the application of this type of technology is Facebook Reality Labs, so-named as their focus is on both virtual and augmented reality. Their scope in the augmentation of humanity is similarly broad and comprehensive. Their shopping list of ideas to develop is "all the technologies needed to enable breakthrough augmented reality glasses and virtual reality headsets, including optics and displays, brain-computer interface, eye, hand, face, and body tracking, perception science, and finally, true telepresence."[426] If these goals are ultimately successful, we are heading to a future where your senses will struggle to detect a discernible difference between the digital world they create and the physical world you currently live in. Therefore, there will be an equal challenge between discerning digital ideas and those created in the real world.

In Hangzhou China, Zhejiang University has already proceeded with human clinical trials for its evolving BMI. Beginning in 2006 with lab-based animal trials, it took less than fifteen years to apply their technology to the minds of human volunteers. They received permission from patients, who had been recently paralysed, to connect their brain's motor cortex to an artificial external prosthesis such as an electronically powered hand. With training, they would first think of grasping a plate of food, a fork or a cup. These thoughts would then spark neurones in their brain, which would be then translated into the specific actions in the electronic prosthesis by the BMI. Patients who had been paralysed for years, were able to learn to feed themselves again and perform other basic, but essential tasks. This provided them with a small form of valued independence while they were connected to the device.[427] The city of Hangzhou is one of the leading innovation hubs of China and home to the dominant technology giant, Alibaba which also have a strong strategic partnership with Zhejiang University, designed to develop and commercialise innovation to strengthen China.[428]

There are many other well-funded companies moving at speed to develop intellectual property in the BMI space. Highly active companies include Kernel, Neurable, Emotiv, CorrActions, Nextmind, and Meltin. The last is a Tokyo-based company that doesn't pull any punches when it comes to its bold ambitions. Meltin articulates that its mission is to design technology to help the human brain create better ideas. Their stated corporate purpose is to "develop Cyborg Technology for envisioning the world where we can maximise creativity."[429] Ironically, the concept of a "cyborg" itself stems from science fiction comics in the 1960s.[430] It was imagined as a cybernetic organism, a seamless and enhanced blend of technology and living biology resulting in incredible, almost superhuman powers. Just fifty years ago, this very idea was simply placed on bookshelves with dog-eared pages, with the same technical credibility and believability as the fellow fictional character, Superman. It was all just pure fantasy. Today, this idea of blending biology with technology is a booming industry valued at over $1.36 billion, backed by some of the most influential minds and companies on the planet. It is projected to nearly triple in value and reach $3.85 billion by 2027.[431]

The long-term future for BMI is highly promising, hopefully it will hack our inherent biological flaws, failures, and weaknesses. Many physical and psychological problems may ultimately be solved forever. Paralysis and Parkinson's disease could become as extinct as Polio, and inflictions like Alzheimers could be bypassed with signals re-routed and memories restored. However, It may not stop with eradicating the many disabilities and illnesses that define the human condition. In theory, it could be used for the enhancement of humanity as well. In fact Elon Musk's stated vision for Neuralink extends to a "full brain-machine interface" that will achieve a "symbiosis with artificial intelligence (AI)."[432] In that far-envisaged, but increasingly possible future, not only could a person load into their biological mental algorithms an unparalleled cloud of instantaneous information and data, they could also game-play millions of potential outcomes in a millisecond, to determine the very best outcome. They could simultaneously and silently transmit and translate the exhaustive data packet, of both the ideas and outcomes, to all similarly augmented colleagues on the planet, so that they could also instantly comprehend the same idea, context, and decision. In this futuristic, hyper-augmented world, the speed to create new ideas, the quality of those ideas and the global alignment on the right idea will dramatically surpass anything that humanity has yet experienced and will be infinitely beyond anything that the sloths of genetic evolution imagined for us.

These approaches may also create the challenge of at least a "two-speed world". Already there are massive disparities in global equality, no-matter whether it's defined by income, opportunity, race, gender, age, health and access to technology. What might be the impact on our civilisation if a single income class, a specific country, or even a political group, takes a significant lead in implementing a ground-breaking augmented, AI-enabled, BMI to take advantage of their competitors? In this scenario, if an early-elite group of AI BMI adopters are ahead of the trailing pack of society, by even just a few years, the inequalities and consequences could be dramatic or at best, very unpredictable. Especially if the motivations and morality behind the first movers are not pure.

It would be like a modern army arriving in ancient Rome, armed with assault rifles, tanks, predator drones, smart missiles, and stealth bombers. How long would it be before they take over and build a brand new society, based on their superior ideas? That hypothetical Roman revolution would be executed in days instead of decades. Would a minority population of fully AI-augmented "BMI" humans unleash a series of universal blessing for our planet? Would their newly augmented ideas be breakthroughs designed to unilaterally eradicate injustice, inequality and illness for everyone? Ushering a new age of peace and balance for society? Or would they create incredible blessings for only themselves, the very first group of truly AI-augmented people? Would their ideas be immediately self-serving and engineered to build protection for their new superiority, resources, or even national interests?

A competing idea to achieve similar objectives in improving humanity beyond our existing biology, is the gene-editing technology, Crispr-Cas9. This is a beautifully simple, yet powerful technology, that can be used for editing genomes in humans, animals, or plants. It allows scientists and industries to efficiently alter DNA sequences and modify gene functions.[433] The potential to develop this technology to adjust both physical abilities and correct genetic defects could potentially create a future segment of the population, genetically superior to ordinary mortals. This possibility is already emerging, and is currently called "gene-doping." Whether individual intelligence can also be manipulated in this manner is still unclear. For the editing to be successful, the trait needs to be genetically inherited at a very high level. Research has shown that many diseases are hereditary to a degree of 90%, and muscle power by around 70%. These make ideal candidates for gene editing technology and even embryo enhancement. Intelligence, however, can be determined by inherited DNA by as little as 50%. This means that nutrition, education, lifestyle, and environment are just as important as the underlying genes themselves in determining a person's total intelligence.[434]

With the current speed at which our augmented BMI and Crispr-Cas9 technology is progressing, combined with the limited oversight, regulations, and predictably uneven adoption of any new innovation, humanity over the next one hundred years, will be confronted by enhanced and augmented versions of our biologic beings. That is assuming that this emerging industry makes the leaps in technologies in a speed rapid enough for humanity to take advantage of these ideas. Unfortunately, the very real alternative is that many of the future ideas that will govern our world, may not be augmented in partnership with humanity, but created completely without our direct involvement. This future may come from one of our newest ideas, called Artificial General Intelligence (AGI). It will be designed to think and learn independently, laterally, creatively, and instantaneously. It may even operate totally independently of our biology, and perhaps outside any of our opinions, filters and, ideas we may have wanted to throw into the digital pot. It's not here yet, but it is an idea that many people, companies, and nations are urgently and aggressively working on.

CHAPTER 12

ARTIFICIAL IDEAS.

Apparently, one of the reasons why Elon Musk is über keen to combine human biology with his nascent Neuralink technology, is that he is legitimately worried as to what will happen to our civilisation if someone doesn't. He has been quoted at major public conferences warning; "I am very close to the cutting edge in AI and it scares the hell out of me. It's capable of vastly more than almost anyone knows and the rate of improvement is exponential. Mark my words, AI is far more dangerous than nukes."[435] It could be argued that the epicentre of his concerns is not the concentration of the exponential abundance of data, information, or computing power, as all this already exists in both excessive and accessible forms. He may be worried about new ideas that a fully autonomous artificial intelligence will suddenly create from this abundance of data, and then instantly implement to the benefit of itself, a narrow group, or even the planet, but not necessarily for the bulk of humanity.

He may also be legitimately worried that these future ideas flowing from an AGI will result in humanity becoming viewed as either second-class citizens, or expendable to this superior intelligence. What would be the outcome of another entity on the planet, with the ability to form millions of ideas in a microsecond, and immediately calculate which of those ideas would lead to the optimal outcome by instantaneously drawing on all the data on every server across the internet? What would happen if that entity was equal in intelligence to humans, or twice as smart, or perhaps even exponentially smarter than your average fry cook or NASA engineer? Which of the AGI's millions of ideas would then take priority and dominance in a given scenario? Perhaps what could be more intriguing on a long-term basis, who's ideas would begin to lead the future of the planet? Human ideas or AGI's? We may not have long to wait before our own intelligence succeeds in creating a form of AGI and we are flooded with answers to these questions as soon as it is switched on.

In research led by professors from Oxford and Yale University, and aggregating opinions from over 350 of the world's leading AI researchers, the projection is that it certainly won't be tomorrow but it might be the day after. They predict that AI will outperform a person in translating languages by 2024, writing high-school essays by 2026, working in retail by 2031, writing a bestselling book by 2049, and operating as a surgeon by 2053. According to this research, there is a 50% chance of AI outperforming humans in all tasks in the next forty-five years and moving onto automating every job any human has, within 120 years.[436] If these assumptions are correct, then peer beyond this relatively short time-period of a single generation. Where will the AGI technology be in 500 or 1,000 years, given that it may also be able to improve its own intelligence at an exponential rate? How much will humans have genetically evolved to keep pace, if at all? The technological ideas that we are creating will be capable of massively evolving themselves, at a pace that outstrips our incredible but slow-witted biological evolution.

The key point to absorb from this research is not if, but when, will this super AGI be born. Much of the consensus from the scientific community indicates the inevetnibilty of artificial intelligence, and therefore there must logically exist a parallel path of new ideas also becoming "artificial". Even if current projections are inaccurate and it takes significantly longer, it seems that it will ultimately be inevitable. Additionally, at the glacier pace of evolutionary timescales, equality of artificially created ideas with biologically created ones will happen within the relative blink of an eye. Resistance by people to at least sharing the future of all ideas may well be futile.

Once an AGI starts conceiving ideas, the human race will still have billions of people, each coming up with ingenious ideas every day. There could develop a competitive reality between humans, and perhaps a limited number of artificial super-intelligent entities that generate millions of ideas every second. The contrast, clash, collaboration, and resolution of ideas, with those of an intellectual equal, has not been seen on this planet since we last exchanged ideas with the Neanderthals, and they have been extinct for over 40,000 years. Since then, we have had the world of ideas all to ourselves. The good, the bad, and even the very ugly ideas, all ours. A complete planet-wide monopoly of ideas that has been unchallenged for millennia, may soon be disrupted by genuine competition, not limited by the frailties of biology, the slow creep of evolution, or the inherent subjectivity and individual variance of humanity's mental algorithms.

This may sound as dystopian as a Kubrick flick, but it may be an extremely positive outcome for our species. In the same way that it could be argued that humanity would save lives by handing road safety decisions over to an AI, there could be countless other areas where our lives would be improved by relinquishing some, or perhaps all, of the governing ideas for the planet, to a less conflicted, subjective, passionate but data driven, vastly superior, artificial intelligence. It may focus its ideas on solutions that are aimed at longer-term outcomes rather than the immediate, narrow, and materialistic motives that plague our political processes. Medicine, surgery, diseases, climate change, pollution, exploration, physics, resource management, agriculture, poverty, malnutrition, and equality of opportunity are all areas that may be dramatically advanced by the unique insights and ideas generated by a future AGI taking a multi-generational and borderless view. An AGI, however, would not likely be perfect, or create a utopia. There would be conflicts and mistakes made in the decision-making processes, just as there are currently errors in autonomous driving algorithms which have led to accidents, and even deaths, when humans have no control.[437] The fundamental equation to be solved is whether, if we gave responsibility to a super-intelligent AGI to lead key industries, with much less human involvement, would it deliver a more positive outcome then leaving ideas and decisions in the subjective hands of governments, corporations, and selfish motivations of influential individuals? It's not a question of whether humans can handle challenging concepts, we clearly can, and have done so brilliantly, and better than any species in history. It's a question of whether people, or an AGI, would excel at creating new ideas in many critical sectors. Some of which, like climate change, were a direct consequence of the ill-conceived ideas of humans.

A massive amount of capital has recently been invested in the idea of driverless cars. For example, "Waymo" which was spun out of Google's driverless car program, has alone already acquired US$2.25 billion in investment to provide it's marketers and engineers with the resources to create solutions for largely eliminating humans from the driving equation.[438] Their mission statement is not overly-focussed on the grubby idea of monetisation, but the nobility of saving humans from the errors of their fellow humans, by creating an intelligence that can operate at a level above any single person on the planet, as it reads: "The Waymo Driver can improve the world's access to mobility while saving thousands of lives now lost to traffic crashes. We are building the World's Most Experienced Driver™."[439]

In the automotive sector, many companies are operating on the principle that human decision-making is often unpredictable, unreliable, and imperfect, and that an AI would be better placed to take responsibility for decisions than a human, for our safety and preservation. Why would other critical socio-economic segments, that dramatically impact millions of lives, be treated and invested in any differently? Surely, the same principle could be applied? Given access to as much capital, technology, and fluffy mission statements, would our civilisation be significantly and objectively improved if we allowed AGI to grab other important socio-economic wheels and relegate humanities' relatively inconsistent decision-making ability to ride in the passenger seat? What about a simple, but essential, and globally critical subject such as our food supply?

Unicef estimates that 3.1 million children die each year from malnutrition.[440] That's nearly 8,500 young souls every day. In the minute it would have taken you to read this page, at least five innocent children would have painfully died from a largely preventable and treatable problem. It is a global crisis that kills more than double the amount of people than road deaths every hour, every day, and every year. This crisis often has uncontrollable external natural factors that seriously contribute to the problem such as cyclones, floods, and droughts, but in many cases, both the cause and the solution is firmly in human hands. Loss of biodiversity, climate change, war, politics, corruption, lack of infrastructure, supply-chain management, and economic imbalance all have the greedy, finger-licking fingerprints of humanity smeared all over it. In 2015, the United Nations (UN) adopted several universally important ideas, contained in their Sustainability Development Goals. Number two in the list, was "Zero Hunger" which was defined as the ambition to end hunger by 2030 and to "ensure access by all people, in particularly the poor, and people in vulnerable situations, including infants, to safe, nutritious, and sufficient food all year round."[441] Unfortunately, despite all genuine efforts, we don't seem to have the united global ability, or the will, to align on which of the available ideas must be soon implemented to meet this essential goal to end hunger and save millions of lives.

This gap between goals and achievements is laid bare in the 2020 Global Nutrition Report, which states; "The trend is clear, progress is too slow to meet the global targets. Not one country is on course to meet all ten of the 2025 global nutrition targets and only a pitiful 8 of 194 countries are on track to meet 40% of the targets. Progress on malnutrition is not just too slow, it is also deeply unfair. New analysis shows that global and national patterns mask significant inequalities within countries and populations, with the most vulnerable groups being most affected."[442] Translate this bureaucratic blancmange into a more common vernacular and it reads, the poor are starving to death while the juicy rich, get fatter. However, the good news, is that as a species, we are on track to ensure that many rich people will soon be able to safely add their hash-browned burgers to their rapidly clogging arteries, while simultaneously tweeting profanities in their autonomous cars, engineered to independently make the important decisions that safely drives them to their local strip-club.

This materialistic irony shines a very harsh light on another dynamic in the battle to fight malnutrition and save lives on Earth. In the same Global Nutrition Report, it indicates that the prevalence of obesity is not declining as both desired or planned. Based on their projections, the likelihood of the planet meeting the desired target of halting the rise in obesity by 2025, is currently at zero.[443] As one section of humanity starves to death, another feeds themselves to excess. The insanity of this idea is not just the volume and type of food that the western world over-consumes, but the levels at which good food is wasted would make even Caligula blush. In the US alone, estimates are that 30-40% of the total food supply is wasted at a yearly cost of US$161 Billion.[444] If properly redirected and managed, it is estimated that there is enough food waste produced every year to feed an additional two billion people.[445] Given that there are an estimated 815 million people that are suffering from malnutrition on the planet[446] there is already more than enough food produced to save millions of lives, while still not infringing on the rights of rich nations to be even plumper if they choose. This social dichotomy may seem deliciously obvious on paper, but it may be very distasteful to the subjective opinions of different groups. For example, in the USA, one of the ideas recommended by politicians for managing food waste is to actively divert it to animal feed, as it is a much more positive alternative to adding to land-fill.[447] It's one of the reasons that swine that live close to Las Vegas are lucky enough to dine daily on rejected lobster, oysters, and beef.[448] They gorge on the mulched excessive left-overs trucked to them from the glamorous "all-you-can-eat" buffets, enticingly designed to fill gamblers stomachs, while the insatiable Casinos surreptitiously empty their wallets.

This appalling arrangement of over-feeding a select group of pigs, while an estimated 8,500 children starve every day is an example of a completely inhuman, human idea that is passively ignored by the majority of our planet's minds on a daily basis, despite the United Nation's pledge for the opposite. However, If we were to delegate this problem to a future AGI, would it subsequently calculate and execute a different, more equitable, outcome that both saved lives, and protected Casino profits? Would an advanced AGI ponder the existing devastating inequalities of the global food supply chain and create fresh ideas that would re-organise the distribution of all existing calories to offer less death and more prosperity across the planet? Perhaps so. If the projections are to be believed, we could have the technology to achieve these types of ideas within one hundred years. At that time, would all the governments and corporations readily accept and implement a transformative idea given their conflicting national objectives and political narratives? Or would there be more votes, profitability, and capital investment, for ideas designed to feed the rich, then for ideas designed to solve the life and death challenges of desperate starving children. If the objective was to improve balance, life-expectancy, and equality in the world, where else would a super AGI succeed with its ideas over ours?

In the future, the limitations to solving our most important problems may not be a shortage of breakthrough ideas that enhance, rather than curtail social development, it may be the inability for humanity to agree to allow a super AGI the freedom to execute these revolutionary ideas and solve these problems. However, the incredible potential if we do embrace the ideas of future super AGI is exciting and limitless to solve the world's challenges, save lives, and create unparalleled prosperity. The choice is still ours, for now.

Of course, popular culture commonly portrays the more threatening aspect of a sentient AGI, via the cinematic narrative that it will systematically wipe out all of humanity without morality or mercy, as it instantly embraces the very human idea of war. Unfortunately, our civilisation is unlikely to even have the patience to wait for a future AGI to decide to wage its destruction. Our society already has very itchy trigger fingers that rapidly militarises new ideas whenever it comes to the business of killing people more efficiently. This has already been made evident on numerous occasions, including the redeployment of early punch card technology to assist the Nazi's tabulate the horrors of the holocaust[449], as well the world's first true computer being funded by the US Military to better calculate and execute targets.[450]

The idea of weaponising a nuclear reaction was used offensively to end World War II in Japan over nine years before it was first used for the more peaceful purposes in Russia as the energy source of a power-station.[451] It wasn't until 1958, when American scientists turned their first Nuclear Power-station on in Shippingport Pennsylvania.[452] In that same period, following the end of World War II and the ignition of that power plant, the US, UK, and Russian defence departments managed to find the time to detonate a total of at least two hundred nuclear bombs to push the art of war relentlessly forward. That's more than one nuclear explosion every month for thirteen years running.[453]

History seems destined to repeat, perhaps because it is people who are the recidivists and don't always remember the lessons from the previous generations' failed ideas. Already, the most dominant military minds of the world are mimicking the nuclear arms race with an entirely new one. Which is, to create the best ideas, in utilising AI to secure a competitive edge in the theatre of battle. This AI arms race, conducted mostly in stealth, has been heating up over the last decade. Arguably the "success" derived from the US Military's deep investment in Predator drone technology, frequently used in Middle-East combat, was the emerging catalyst for an increased focus in this area. Perhaps the most public sign that this new arms race had started was when Russian President Vladimir Putin publicly stated in 2017 that "whoever reaches a breakthrough in developing artificial intelligence will come to dominate the world."[454] It's a safe guess to assume that he would make every bare-chested, horse-ridding effort to ensure Russia holds the reins.

By most accounts, Russia is actually running behind on the AI development curve, but following Putin's statements, Russia is seeking to accelerate their position by setting both five and ten-year targets in advancing their AI expertise, datasets, infrastructure investment, and legal regulatory systems. One of their early areas of strategic investment was on autonomous ground, air, and sea vehicles that could operate independently, and target the enemy, ultimately engaging with lethal autonomy.[455] In 2018, Russia actively deployed their first weaponised autonomous vehicle, the Uran-9, in Syria for testing. This was armed with a medium calibre machine-gun together with anti-tank missiles which were remotely controlled by human operators. It reportedly failed on most of its mission parameters, so there is clearly more upgrades and innovation yet to be completed.[456] It will, however, need to be accomplished with haste, as Russia's Military-Industrial Committee has a public goal to derive 30% of Russia's total combat power from remote-controlled AI systems and platforms by 2030.[457] Additionally, and what may be even more of a destabilising threat, Russia is reported to be focussing on using AI to enhance cyberwar to aid the further distribution of propaganda ideas and accelerate social, psychological, and intelligence operations to disrupt their enemies.[458]

Competing ideas from China, on the utility of AI in war, are further advanced than their Russian counterparts. At a 2018 session of the Chinese Politburo, their Premier, Xi Jinping, made the national agenda clear with the aggressively ambitious goal to ensure that China "marches in the front ranks where it comes to theoretical research in the important area of AI, and occupies the high ground in critical and core technologies." [459] China has subsequently set a goal to lead the world in AI by 2030 in a program called the "New Generation AI Development Plan" issued by the State Council. Although they may currently trail the US in development and research, they have been investing in a vibrant AI infrastructure and technology eco-system that they can align to aid their strategic development. Companies like Alibaba and Tencent all have significant investment in this area, and research indicates that China has at least ten AI-focussed tech start-ups that are valued at over US$1 billion each. They also have the world's second-largest pool of available AI engineers with an estimated nearly 20,000 available, compared to nearly 30,000 in the USA.[460] While this volume of talent is distributed across many private and industrial sectors, the weaponisation of AI to strengthen China's position will undoubtedly get its share of focus and investment. China's National Defence white paper highlights the importance of pursuing this objective and the seismic shifts in power that it may potentially yield, saying: "Driven by the new round of technological and industrial revolution, the application of cutting-edge technologies such as artificial intelligence, quantum information, big data, cloud computing and the Internet of things is gathering pace in the military field. International military competition is undergoing historic changes."[461]

The seismic National necessity of leading the technological AI arms race seems both clear and urgent to the Chinese Military. Leading Chinese-made autonomous weaponry is already being actively promoted and marketed at trade shows in China and abroad. Guangdong-based weapons company, Zhuhai Ziyan UAV, launched its helicopter drone in 2019, the "BlowFish A2" equipped with mortar shells, grenade launchers, and machine-guns. They are about the size and weight of a family Labrador, and can travel up to 130km per hour with a range of 80km. They are enabled with "intelligent swarm technology" designed for wireless co-ordination with up to ten other drones for combined attacks on designated targets or even "suicide" runs.[462] The makers of the BlowFish A2 suggest that it can be operated in a fully autonomous mode, with no human involvement in decision making, if or when needed. These types of "just set and forget" technologies are termed "Lethal Autonomous Weapon Systems" or "LAWS" by the arms-industry and are under rapid development in many countries. Indeed, both Pakistan and Saudi Arabia are reported to be interested in buying the BlowFish A2 and others are likely to review its capabilities.[463] They are a great idea to make killing more convenient, and also the perfect gift idea for any busy international terrorist who may not specifically want to travel to a location to blow it up. Now they can simply send an explosive swarm of the BlowFish A2 instead.

Unfortunately, this is not such a good idea for the people targeted by LAWS such as these, and similar future innovations. They may be virtually impossible to restrict to just a traditional battlefield. They may eventually be weaponised to "swarm" in our cities, schools, offices, sporting events, and anywhere else by any group with funds, agenda, and a target. Naturally, this swelling tsunami of an AI arms race has not escaped the mighty scrutiny of the US Military. In 2019, the US Secretary of Defence, Mark Esper made a public speech at the National Security Commission on Artificial Intelligence, warning of both the urgency and the necessity for the US to combat this growing threat, with the statement; "While the US faces a mighty task in transitioning the world's most advanced military to new AI-enabled systems, China believes it can leapfrog our current technology and go straight to the next generation. Advances in AI have the potential to change the character of warfare for generations to come. Whichever nation harnesses AI first, will have a decisive advantage on the battlefield for many, many years. We have to get there first."[464]

Not surprisingly, the US Department of Defence has allocated around US$1 billion per year to AI projects, and has established a dedicated task-force to co-ordinate AI development across various departments, called the Joint Artificial Intelligence Center (JAIC).[465] Other reports indicate that as much as US$4 billion is being spent annually across the US military, and some analysts have argued that this needs to urgently escalate to US$25 billion.[466] How much is already being spent on secret programs is not publicly known, but it's legitimate to speculate that there are many other significant "black" AGI projects tinkering within the Pentagon. One area where the US is at a disadvantage to China is leveraging the significant AI expertise within the private sector.

A 2017 survey of leading US Tech companies illustrated a strong cultural gap between the Department Of Defence and the more liberal ideas of Silicon Valley employees. Nearly 80% of participants believed that the tech community's relationship with the Department of Defence was either "poor" or "very poor".[467] Famously, in 2018, Google employees were appalled at the idea of collaborating on a Pentagon program called "Project Maven". Its mission was to build an AI-powered surveillance platform for unmanned aerial vehicles which could include technology such as LAWS. Over 3,000 employees protested to Google management, who was compelled to reset some of their engagements with the US Military, while still maintaining their belief in the importance of National Defence, and to work for peace and safety.[468] It is unlikely that similar AI engineering companies in Russia, Iran or China would have the same ability to set their own terms to their respective governments, or push back on official State requests to apply their corporate ideas on new generation AI weapon systems, in the best interest of national defence. The US may have a further hill to climb compared to other nations. A pesky legal code. The U.S. Congress has mandated that a human needs to be directly involved in targeting decisions in any LAWS system. The US Department of Defence supports this and have issued an additional directive that people should have the final decision for target engagement.[469] As of 2021, neither the governments of China or Russia has implemented a complementary idea.

The UN has called for a complete international ban on the development of LAWS without human intervention. In 2019, the UN Secretary-General, António Guterres, stated that "machines with the power and discretion to take lives, without human involvement, are politically unacceptable, morally repugnant and should be prohibited by international law".[470] While these platitudes received resounding nods of support from many diplomats in the international community, the key AI innovators in the world, UK, Israel, USA, China, and Russia appear to be placing their emerging autonomous ideas in a convenient legal loophole. They often argue that existing international law is adequate or they state that perhaps the active field use of LAWS against enemy combatants should indeed be banned, but in the meantime, the research and development in AI weaponry, and creation of the technology should not be precluded.[471] This is diplomatic speak, to convey that our species would rather invent the next level of deadly, efficient and autonomous AI weapons, and then decide when to use them, instead of agreeing to regulations stopping their invention in the first place. This means that we are inexorably at the start of the next global arms race. A world where our civilisation will rapidly invent and engage in a race to perfectly design AI-based LAWS to efficiently and autonomously kill members of our own species for economic, territorial or political purposes. We don't need to wait until humanity invents a super AGI robot and then watch it unilaterally, consciously, and independently have its own ideas for mass killing people. Our Governments and military are inventing this, right now. We are deliberately cutting out the deadly middle-man, or in this case, the middle-AI-robot.

This from of insanity shouldn't be a surprise to anyone. Indeed, it wouldn't be to the principal architect of the Atomic era's Mutually Assured Destruction (MAD) theory, John Von Neumann, if only he were still alive today to see it. As previously discussed, his ideas on Game Theory predicted that the only strategic way to survive our most destructive atomic ideas was, for all sides to have the obscene capacity to completely and instantly annihilate each other and thus, create an uneasy and threatening equilibrium.[472] The world's super-powers may now be currently replaying the same Von Neumann playbook when it comes to weaponising AI. Revolutionary and aggressive advances in LAWS are escalating to a point where this proliferation will probably eventually lead to either one nation dominating, through a first-mover advantage, or our Planet becoming locked in another MAD stand-off, replicating the 1960s Cold War. If the latter eventuates, the strategy might potentially succeed and create a balanced tension of nervous geopolitical peace, interspersed with blazing rhetoric and dangerous pressure points similar to the Cuban Missile Crisis of the Kennedy era. Any hot disputes may be eventually settled by low-tech wars, using conventional weapons. It may also seep into all aspects of our community and culture, just as living under the fear of the "mushroom cloud" was widespread for decades in society.

A very real and worrying difference is that the atomic bomb was never going to have ideas of its own. As advanced as the atomic bomb was, it had zero decision-making ability and therefore, was ultimately at our mercy. We are now on an innovation path where we are creating extraordinarily deadly weaponry that will be, at first, automated but then eventually, may be designed to generate ideas of its own and make aggressive targeting decisions accordingly. This may take another thirty or one hundred years of AI development but on all current trajectory, our species will eventually accomplish this level of innovation. We seemingly are hungry to learn how to apply it in warcraft, with our usual relish and speed, and perhaps well in advance of many other peaceful and beneficial AGI applications.

How will a weaponised super AGI change the global geopolitical dynamics? Especially one that may be hard to eliminate, could kamikaze in battle, or operate in mass swarms? It could also be responsible for deciding who is expendable at the speed of microseconds. The outcome of this dramatic technological trajectory can not be predicted with any degree of accuracy. Also, imagine that a military power invents, and then tasks, a super-AGI to create bold new ideas on how to engineer even more efficient weapons to eliminate enemy populations of people when required? What will the outcome be then for maintaining a balance in a MAD strategy? Humanity is playing with a very deadly box of matches and our only historical strategy for maintaining peace is currently one based on a game of bluff no more sophisticated than a Las Vegas poker player playing Texas hold-em. We survived the 1960s with this approach, but if we don't survive the next chapter of idea evolution with this strategy, to deal with escalating weaponry, we will only have ourselves to blame, as it was our insane ideas that drove us to invent our own execution.

Do we use our newest, best, and most intelligent ideas, like AI, to solve massive problems like climate change, equality, starvation, and peace? Or do we first deploy them against one another to score points, take resources, build borders and inflate egos. It will ultimately be our choice, and not an AGI's, despite what Hollywood sells you.

CHAPTER 13

WHAT'S NEXT?

In the absence of a dramatic new dynamic or unexpected pressure from an external intervention, we should assume that the firmly established socio-economic models that generated this advanced point in civilisation, will continue to determine the immediate future as well. As the ancient Chinese proverb predicts, If we do not change direction, we may end up where we are heading. It is reasonable to expect that society will continue to create, claw, and climb upon the growing cacophony of both beautiful and bizarre ideas that we have been building over time. This mountain has been founded on human ingenuity blended with the long-term mega-trends of population growth, urbanisation, declining poverty, instant connectivity, exponential technologies, borderless media, tribalism, politics, nationalism, and even some good-old-fashioned greed.

Just over the horizon are scores of amazing ideas that will cure diseases, squeeze efficiencies, reduce pollution and save lives. To balance this, unfortunately, there will be many that are clinically calculated to take lives more efficiently or limit the potential of millions in the community. In this turbulent, cluttered and fast-moving environment it will be challenging, but not impossible, for people, companies and governments to seamlessly gravitate towards the ideas that only generates increased clarity, balance, and equality with a high degree of certainty. Although the correct path may be challenging to find, the consequences of getting ideas wrong, in an infinitely connected world, is escalating in parallel with the power of our technology. To add complexity to this, the immense carousel of total possible choices is multiplying by the day.

Ultimately we may need to design better systems to dramatically optimise the odds in our favour, and reduce the substantial risk from confusion and errors. Inspiringly, we've been here before, in the crossfire of a crisis, and found bold ideas, leading to solutions that drove national prosperity and increased balance for decades.

During the devastation of the 1930s Great Depression, thousands of businesses went broke, banks were closed, and fifteen million Americans, over 20% of the US population, were desperately unemployed.[473] The turbulence and panic in the markets, bucked and kicked the world economy continuously to 1933 when Franklin D. Roosevelt was elected as United States President. He attempted to restore calm and exorcise the economic demons, with his often echoed words "we have nothing to fear, except fear itself." In addition to the power of rhetoric, his new administration searched for innovative ideas to help empower fiscal policy and combat the financial paranoia and turmoil. At the time, the available economic data was completely fragmented, siloed, and often contradictory. The Government required a more holistic perspective to take control, direct economic policy and yield insights so a more stable National development course could be charted.

In 1934, when addressing this challenge, the US Congress listened to the ideas from a University of Pennsylvania Economist, the Belarus-born, Simon Kuzent. He shared with the Senators his new methodology for agglomerating a country's economic activity to arrive at a unified set of national accounts, which would better indicate the relative growth of an economy across a given period. The politicians embraced the idea as a panacea to their ills and the concept of Gross Domestic Product (GDP) was soon injected into policy. By 1944, it had been adopted by multiple countries as a key barometer of economic growth and, therefore, overall national prosperity.

The global importance of this idea was captured by Nobel laureate, Paul Samuelson, and William Nordhaus with their observation that GDP "enables the President, Congress, and the Federal Reserve to judge whether the economy is contracting or expanding, whether the economy needs a boost or should be reined in a bit, and whether a severe recession or inflation, threatens. Without measures of economic aggregates like GDP, policymakers would be adrift in a sea of unorganised data. The GDP and related data are like beacons that help policymakers steer the economy toward the key economic objectives."[474] GDP was an all-encompassing measurement of growth and once adopted, the idea of governing by the winds of constant expansion became central to policy and nations. The economic true-north of relentlessly aligning a nation's resources to pursue increasing GDP, in a rapidly expanding industrial world, certainly increased economic stability, while generating continuous growth.

During the years following World War II, and the adoption of GDP as a governing measure, the length of the average economic downturn was halved to just eleven months, with a contraction occurring on average once every five years, instead of the previous three.[475] In the many decades of economic expansion since the 1940s, billions of people worldwide have been elevated out of poverty. In 1950, there were just 2.5 billion people on the planet, and incredibly 63% were living in extreme poverty. By 2015, the population of the Earth had swelled to 7.35 billion people, but despite this surge, less than 10% were living in these desperate circumstances.[476] In the same period, the world capitalised on many other incredible ideas to deliver near-miraculous advances in numerous segments such as medicine, transportation, energy, trade, and information technology. The 20th Century industrial engine, governed by the gods of growth and evaluated by GDP, has been nothing short of transformational. Simon Kuzent's idea, which helped focus the world on this key metric, arguably played a pivotal role in creating stability and prosperity for the entire planet. It is an idea that has been almost universally adopted across the majority of countries in the world, despite the tremendous differences in geographies, currencies, religions, culture, competing systems of governments and even wars. GDP is a rare example of almost total global alignment, on a single idea, at truly massive scale for nearly one-hundred years.

However, this incredible economic journey has simultaneously been decidedly unbalanced and exceedingly rewarding for an elite minority. For example, the richest twenty-two men in the world now have more wealth than all the women in Africa, and the 2,100 billionaires living large on their yachts have more wealth than the poorest 4.6 billion people on Earth can scrounge together.[477] The Amazon Founder, Jeff Bezos, at one point, had a net worth more than the GDP of 140 of the world's 195 countries.[478] Income inequality, in industrial countries, is disturbingly still on the rise. Unfortunately, the reverse was predicted by Simon Kuzent's economic models, but the raw data shines a harsh light on a very different reality. In 1983, the upper income of US society held 60% of the aggregate wealth. This has now ballooned to almost 80%, at the pain and expensive of the low and middle-income Americans who have lost considerably.[479] While the unquestioned pursuit of GDP growth has created significant benefits for billions of people around the world, the system has additionally created obscenely deep pockets in income inequality as well. There are no signs of the luxuriously lucrative pool of caviar and gravy running dry, anytime soon.

Collectively, we have also manifested some of this wealth by heavily mortgaging the future, pushing the risk towards following generations. Our planet is now approximately US$277 trillion in debt.[480] This is almost four times the annual economic output of the entire world and each man, woman and child is currently on the hook for over US$37,000 each. Presumably, every penny will need to be paid back at some stage, by someone, somewhere down the line.

Economic strength and national prosperity, defined by GDP are so pervasive and successful that it now might seem like an immutable fiscal idea, that was created by unquestionable policy prophets and cast in eternal economic stone. However, there have been alternative ideas, previously circulated, and debated for consideration. These and other ideas may now be increasingly relevant to the emerging challenges, faced by our society, as we now may not require systems that incentivises an endless abundance of ideas, devoid of purpose, and blind to any consequences from that growth. We may now require national strategies, no longer anchored in the undefined materialism of unlimited growth, but one that actively seeks to segment the ideas we create, so that economic forces will automatically prioritise those that positively contribute towards the enhancement of society, and not just the unlimited expansion. One example is the concept of development based upon a metric of "national happiness" and not just boundless growth. This idea has been considered for centuries.

On July 4th in 1776, the thirteen United States of America included the "pursuit of happiness" as an inalienable right that all men must freely pursue. Inexplicably, this inspiring universal principle didn't apply equally to all their fellow humans, as many were held as slaves at the time.[481] Happiness, as a metric, never morphed into a measurement parameter for US economic policy. Despite being prominent in the Bill of Rights, the idea of "maximising happiness", as a governing operating system, laid virtually dormant for many generations until 1968. In that year, the US Presidential Candidate, Robert F Kennedy, began publicly questioning undefined, unlimited growth, as an overarching national goal, as he engaged in a debate to create a new direction for America.

At the University of Kansas in March 1968, during the insanity of the Vietnam War, he called for a purpose driven methodology to help govern the future of the US Nation, with his eloquently powerful, yet damning observations that "Gross National Product counts air pollution, cigarette advertising, and ambulances, to clear our highways of carnage. It counts special locks for our doors and the jails for the people who break them. It counts the destruction of the redwood and the loss of our natural wonder in chaotic sprawl. It counts napalm and counts nuclear warheads and armoured cars for the police to fight the riots in our cities. It counts Whitman's rifle and Speck's knife, and the television programs which glorify violence to sell toys to our children. Yet the Gross National Product does not allow for the health of our children, the quality of their education or the joy of their play. It does not include the beauty of our poetry or the strength of our marriages, the intelligence of our public debate or the integrity of our public officials. It measures neither our wit nor our courage, neither our wisdom nor our learning, neither our compassion nor our devotion to our country, it measures everything, in short, except that which makes life worthwhile. And it can tell us everything about America except why we are proud that we are Americans."[482] His visionary words resonate more insightfully today, then ever before, as we begin to value the quality of ideas over sheer quantity.

For example, our world still counts all the elements that negatively contribute to climate change as part of GDP and, therefore, a measure of a nation's success. As a result, it ultimately rewards and even reinforces the use and impact of fossil fuels and all other components that contribute to global warming. The same is true with any other bad idea that a society and industry automatically invests in. It is extremely likely that its output is tabulated as adding to a nations success, even if it harms it. If we want to promote and prioritise the very best ideas for the future, they need to be evaluated as such, and currently, they are lumped on the GDP pile with all the negative economic ideas. This doesn't necessarily need to be the case. Society could prioritise, incentivise or value investment in a range of balanced and long-term ideas so that a Nation's development is governed in a defined direction and not just in a ballooning, gluttonous one.

In June 1968, just three months after his insightful critique of the soulless measurement of GDP, Robert Kennedy was shot to death at the Ambassador Hotel, in Los Angeles. Any momentum that was gathering for his ideas on changing how we measure growth, and guide a nation, silently died with him.

Four years later, to carry a flickering torch of this type of idea forward, the European Commissioner for Agriculture, Sicco Mansholt, wrote an impassioned letter to the President of the European Commission, suggesting that they replace GDP with a concept that championed Kennedy's views, which he called Gross National Happiness (GNH). Mansholt's idea was almost completely ignored by the Commission. The Bhutanese Government, many decades later, eventually embraced this idea and were the first to establish a GNH index for their country in 2008. Very few other countries have followed their lead.[483] One of the recent exceptions is New Zealand which adopted a "Happiness Index Metric" in 2019, as part of an overall strategy to improve the welfare of the nation as opposed to only worshipping at the pagan altar of GDP growth.[484] The United Nations in 2012, also proudly established the relatively toothless "World Happiness Index" which subjectively measures citizen's perceived level of happiness in a country.[485]

A handful of US states, including Vermont, Colorado, and Hawaii have embraced a derivative of these ideas called the "Genuine Progress Indicator" or GPI.[486] This measure attempts to discount from any traditional calculation of GDP items that do not lead to improving society, but would ordinarily be considered as growth. Examples might be investment into crime, pollution, deforestation, and inequality. Conversely, items that increase the wellbeing of a community, such as renewable energy, security, hospitals, education, volunteering, and child care are seen as generating a positive impact and can be weighted as such.

In all these cases, the agreed areas of prioritisation could, of course, embrace a wide spectrum of ideas that would be traditionally defined as belonging to both the political left or right. A state or a nation could discuss, define, or even vote on a diverse range of ideas that they believe are critically important to driving their society's development, values, safety and progression. The ideas don't have to be just those that appeal to one narrow, political sector or party, they can be bi-partisan and broad, but intelligently, purposely and precisely defined to promote better outcomes for all. Admittedly, the way "happiness index's" seem currently articulated often appear to be overtly left-leaning and driving towards an unbalanced hippy utopia. The key to success is neither left or right, but one of strategy and focus. To move from an obese system of "more of everything and anything", to build a system to focus increased growth on precisely the items and industries each society wants and de-prioritise others that create noise, instability, clutter, inefficiencies and waste.

Although, these scarce initiatives that deviate from GDP, build upon Kennedy's bold vision and Mansholt's idea of GNH, it's not as if there has been a global landslide away from pervasive reliance on GDP during the last fifty years. While there is leaky momentum in small pockets and geography, the flood gates are not likely to open anytime soon, given the current trajectory. Kuzent's concept of GDP still reigns supreme, nearly one hundred years after its invention. If this model, which blindly guides and incentivises the economic development of our civilisation, continues on the idea of pursuing unrelenting and unstoppable GDP growth, then, almost by default, our society will layer further complexities upon the already convoluted structures built to handle this rudderless, limitless and arguably soulless pursuit of "more". Companies and institutions that operate inside these economies will, in aggregate, need to maintain their resolute focus on the growth of output, often in absence of any true measure of the quality or wellness of the output. Ideas, therefore, will continue to be primarily selected for the ability to be monetised and deliver short-term growth, rather than any other intrinsic, long-term value that society might have otherwise placed on them.

That is not to say that there are no people, companies or politicians with good ideas pursuing inspiring agendas within this structure. There absolutely are. However, the reality is that they are competing with the gravity of the GDP economy and, therefore, national policy, lobby groups, economic interests, corporations and stock markets, will continue to be strongly directed by the Gods of unlimited growth. This implies that a global debate on whether the McRib should be permanently available is valued, just as highly as creating ideas to end starvation. The projection for human population growth is that it will continue to expand to 9.7 billion people by 2050. By comparison, the World Wildlife Fund estimates that there are only 500,000 great apes alive today, which is only about the same population of people in Kansas City.[487] Our unchecked human expansion will continue to gorge upon society's existing infrastructure and demand all ideas that monetise and materialise the pursuit of growth. This will ultimately require humanity to add even more urbanisation, density, social connections, technology, and perhaps even increased risk into the world to orchestrate the relentless resources required to filter through the ocean of ideas that will become available just to find the ones that might actually work.

There will be, of course, incredible innovations in efficiency, agriculture, energy production, transportation and utilisation, which will all reduce friction within the system, but it won't change the fact that the underlying objective and purpose of a nation will be defined and fuelled by the melee of growth, with no clear purpose and no allowance for the impact of any immense failures. That means ideas which drive towards accelerating inequality, pollution, selfish interest, armed conflict, and social unrest may be just as likely to be championed by the system as more positive ideas, as long as they lead to continued growth. In this environment, we could potentially see a continuation of the trends that global society is now grappling with, such as the duality of declining poverty rates in parallel with an increasingly intense concentration of elite wealth.

The volume and speed of ideas will continue to grow, fuelled by urbanisation, population growth, connectivity, social exchange platforms, and funded by government policy and capital markets. This will all be desperately needed, to chase down the holy grail of GDP growth to fuel our unlimited expansion. Humanity's underlying biology, physiology, and psychology won't be evolving in this time period to cope with any of this onslaught. Our biological hardware and software is already defined unless it's upgraded artificially with technology. It will need to manage this continuing avalanche of data, ideas, options, and expansion as optimally as possible. To cope with this growing complexity, our track record suggests that, as a species, we will allocate an escalating amount of authority for all the upcoming trillions of daily decisions, to the increasingly intelligent and pervasive technologies that we will create to augment our lives and economies. This may have started in ancient Sumer, with a humble clay counting board, but is now rapidly morphing towards true artificial intelligence. The long-term future potential of this technology may be virtually unlimited in capacity and impact. It is both progressively planned and projected to grow in intelligence until it meets, and then surpasses our ability to imagine and analyse ideas. The exact timeline is not easily defined, but the inevitable trajectory seems abundantly clear and being chased down by the military powers of the world. At the very least, this new from of intelligence will become progressively merged with humanity in the coming decades, in a lab owned by Neuralink, or one of their hungry competitors.

At some point, in this accelerating future, the expansion and eventual "upgrading" of intelligence will relegate any "standard" biological people to being the second-smartest species, or the new Neanderthals of the Planet. At which point, this new class of superior intelligence, be it artificial, or one merged with humanity, will generate new ideas of its own, on how to best select ideas that will generate future outcomes. If this sounds like an Orwellian scenario, it might be, but it doesn't necessarily have to be the outcome. The complete reverse could also be true. This development path could ultimately unleash new clarity and equality in society by progressively solving our most complex and challenging global problems. Truly beautiful ideas could be just around the technological corner.

Simon Kuzent's 1934 idea, to track the progress of a nation based upon his methodology of GDP, is only a single idea created by his own insightful intellect. Although it collectively took humanity thousands of years to first articulate the concept, it is just one potential method to navigate economic development for planet-wide progression. In spite of any flaws, it undeniably helped generate massive stability, prosperity, and even peace across the planet for many decades. Behind all those aggregated GDP numbers, there are billions of people, parents, and families who may have remained in desperate poverty, had their lives cut short, or been dragged into conflict if Kuzent's idea wasn't globally embraced. This doesn't automatically imply that GDP is still the optimum idea for defining success going forward. There could be many other ideas, yet to be imagined and unleashed. Ideas on progression that are more insightful and powerful, could be patiently waiting to be unearthed.

Perhaps an emerging future intelligence, engineered by humanity with technology at its core, will generate the breakthrough creativity and clarity required to build systems that optimise global health and balance, while decreasing discrimination, inequality, pollution, and famine. The same could be true for ideas that govern the concepts of democracy, deployment of capital, resource distribution, energy production, conflict resolution, and climate change. Smarter minds may simply yield smarter ideas. If so, what difference does it make if those ideas run on the hardware of silicon circuits rather than our evolved biological synapses? A good idea, that solves a global challenge, should be embraced, regardless of the creator. Will we be wise enough to let go of society's reins and deploy their innovative opinions?

The legendary Apple Founder, CEO and innovator, Steve Jobs, reportedly once said "It doesn't make sense to hire smart people and tell them what to do; we hire smart people so they can tell us what to do."[488] Leadership coaches and consultants gloriously parrot Steve Jobs' wisdom when advising how companies and leaders should similarly evolve with conviction. The same philosophy and curtesy may also be applied to the next generation of artificial super-intelligence that will submit its credentials for the job of orchestrating our future. Perhaps we should intelligently stand back, and let it lead. Like an insightful CEO, the human race may only need to create, educate, and groom the next generation of intelligence, so it can tell us what is best to do next as a species. There is no shame in this.

The alpha desire of humans to remain in charge may only be only due to the illusion of ego and not focused on increasing optimal outcomes for ourselves and our environment. Like an old champion boxer, still wanting to flail in the ring, after new and fitter competitors have not just taken their gold belt, but beaten their skull into an addled bucket of meat and bone. As there was inherent wisdom in Steve Jobs, delegating the future of his company to the smarter people he recruited, there is no failure in humans employing he same strategy with the smarter intelligence we may eventually create. Is there risk? Yes, of course, there are many, significant and they have been documented extensively by the military, leading scientists, and of course, Hollywood. Any missteps on the journey towards true artificial intelligence could be just as precarious as the final result itself. However, it may be the only logical and intelligent path given the current trajectory that our technology and military is on. The eventual choice may not be whether we should give up a degree of control, but how we best engineer, guide, and educate this new intelligence, that we will ultimately and irresistibly give a degree of control to, like the Sumerians before us. It would not be the first time that our species has shared intellectual space with equals who created competing ideas. Intelligent hominid species like Neanderthals and Denisovans enjoyed the Earth in parallel with our direct ancestors for thousands of years.[489] Many people today carry with them up to 3% Neanderthal DNA in their blood as a result of that collaboration. We interbred with them, merging our intellects and, therefore, entwining our futures forever. If Elon Musk and the other innovators of the Brain Machine Interface succeed with their augmented innovations, history may indeed repeat itself.

What's next? Over the aeons, humans have already proven themselves to be the preeminent idea-machines that the indomitable natural forces of chemistry and evolution has ever created on this planet. It has taken millions of years, and billions of ideas, to arrive at this cumulative point in history. However, the single generation of people that may now create the zenith of all our ideas, a superior intelligence, that instantly creates and assesses its own ideas, may already have been born. The ultimate human idea may be to expertly, and exquisitely curate a new line of smarter, super-intelligent idea machines, integrate with them, and then watch them solve problems before our very eyes. Alternatively, if that idea is judged to be scary, risky or unappealing, we could halt this progression, slow the pace, decrease the noise and re-focus our intellect and ideas on producing quality of ideas and not quantity. We could attempt to redefine human potential based on incentivising better ideas to optimise all life on the planet, and not simply engineering an abundance of growth and expansion. In the process, organise capital, social and political systems to promote ideas that generate long-term prosperity, peace, partnerships, security, balance, and beauty. City by City, State by State, Nation by Nation. This may be exceedingly difficult to accomplish and will take hard work, compromise and collaboration. To add more pressure to this direction, the time available to undertake this transformation is limited by the development of our intelligent technology which is rapidly accelerating and being weaponised, but as Senator Robert Kennedy prophesied in 1962, "The future is not a gift, it is an achievement."[490]

However, If either of these outcomes sounds like insanity, then perhaps someone has a new and even better idea?

INDEX.

NOTES.

1 https://www.famousscientists.org/antoine-lavoisier/
2 https://www.history.com/news/8-things-you-may-not-know-about-the-guillotine
3 https://www.geriwalton.com/being-broken-on-the-wheel-in-the-18th-century/
4 https://www.famousscientists.org/antoine-lavoisier/
5 C N R Rao, Indumati Rao. Lives And Times Of Great Pioneers In Chemistry. 2015
6 https://www.nature.com/articles/137254b0
7 https://www.toureiffel.paris/en/the-monument/eiffel-tower-and-science
8 https://tlexinstitute.com/how-to-effortlessly-have-more-positive-thoughts/
9 https://www.conservation.org/places/birds-head-seascape
10 https://www.genome.gov/25520157/online-education-kit-1859-darwin-published-on-the-origin-of-species-proposing-continual-evolution-of-species
11 Desmond, Adrian & Moore, James. Darwin. 1991
12 Darwin, Charles . On the Origin of Species by Means of Natural Selection, or the Preservation of Favoured Races in the Struggle for Life . 1865.
13 https://www.reuters.com/article/us-vatican-evolution-idUSLG62672220080916
14 http://www.gallup.com/poll/27847/majority-republicans-doubt-theory-evolution.aspx
15 Pew Research Center. 2018
16 https://www.conservation.org/experts-list/mark-erdmann-phd
17 https://www.nhm.ac.uk/discover/shark-evolution-a-450-million-year-timeline.html
18 https://www.conservation.org/blog/discovery-afoot-new-study-cracks-mystery-of-how-walking-sharks-split
19 https://www.discovermagazine.com/planet-earth/humanitys-early-ancestors-were-upright-walking-apes
20 https://www.npr.org/2020/08/13/902157235/everyone-needs-a-buddy-even-sharks
21 https://www.insider.com/shark-myths-untrue-2018-7#myth-sharks-have-tiny-brains-and-are-therefore-dumb-4
22 https://www.livescience.com/57942-what-was-first-life-on-earth.html
23 https://www.britannica.com/biography/Jean-Piaget
24 https://www.smithsonianmag.com/science-nature/the-human-familys-earliest-ancestors-7372974/
25 https://www.karger.com/Article/PDF/272924
26 https://evolution.berkeley.edu/evolibrary/article/evograms_03
27 https://www.newscientist.com/article/dn20035-lost-islands-of-the-crows-revealed-in-dna-study/

28 https://www.smithsonianmag.com/science-nature/ten-curious-facts-about-octo-puses-7625828/

29 Other Minds: The Octopus, the Sea and the Deep Origins of Consciousness, by Peter Godfrey-Smith. 2016

30 https://www.nhm.ac.uk/discover/octopuses-keep-surprising-us-here-are-eight-examples-how.html

31 https://www.ncbi.nlm.nih.gov/pmc/articles/PMC4803207/

32 https://blogs.scientificamerican.com/observations/archaeologists-take-wrong-turn-find-world-s-oldest-stone-tools-update/

33 https://www.smithsonianmag.com/blogs/national-museum-of-natural-histo-ry/2020/04/28/these-decades-biggest-discoveries-human-evolution/

34 https://www.ft.com/content/00a266c2-4ad3-11e7-919a-1e14ce4af89b

35 https://evolution-outreach.biomedcentral.com/articles/10.1007/s12052-010-0247-8

36 https://humanorigins.si.edu/evidence/human-fossils/species/homo-habilis

37 https://humanorigins.si.edu/evidence/human-fossils/species/kenyanthro-pus-platyops

38 https://australian.museum/learn/science/human-evolution/larger-brains/

39 https://www.voanews.com/silicon-valley-technology/earliest-known-human-hand-ax-found-kenya

40 https://www.nature.com/news/million-year-old-ash-hints-at-origins-of-cook-ing-1.10372

41 https://www.nature.com/scitable/knowledge/library/homo-erectus-a-big-ger-smarter-97879043/

42 https://www.nature.com/scitable/knowledge/library/homo-erectus-a-big-ger-smarter-97879043/

43 https://www.telegraph.co.uk/news/2018/02/20/language-started-15m-years-ear-lier-previously-thought-scientists/

44 https://insidescience.org/news/final-days-homo-erectus

45 https://www.sciencedaily.com/releases/2018/08/180810091542.htm

46 https://www.sciencedaily.com/releases/2010/06/100614101724.htm

47 Andrew D. White. A History of the Warfare of Science With Theology in Chris-tendom. 1992

48 https://www.krusecontrolinc.com/examples-of-failure-in-social-network-ing-sites/

49 https://www.sciencemag.org/news/2017/06/world-s-oldest-homo-sapiens-fos-sils-found-morocco

50 https://www.worldometers.info/world-population/world-population-by-year/

51 https://theconversation.com/when-did-we-become-fully-human-what-fossils-and-dna-tell-us-about-the-evolution-of-modern-intelligence-143717

52 https://geology.com/stories/13/volcanic-explosivity-index/

53 https://www.theguardian.com/world/2018/dec/31/new-discoveries-at-pompeii-come-amid-renaissance-at-site

54 https://geology.com/stories/13/volcanic-explosivity-index/

55 https://www.nationalgeographic.com/news/2018/03/toba-supervolcano-eruption-humans-south-africa-science/

56 https://www.livescience.com/29130-toba-supervolcano-effects.html

57 https://pubs.giss.nasa.gov/abs/ro09900j.html

58 https://www.npr.org/sections/krulwich/2012/10/22/163397584/how-human-beings-almost-vanished-from-earth-in-70-000-b-c

59 https://www.sciencedaily.com/releases/2010/08/100817122405.htm

60 https://www.livescience.com/29130-toba-supervolcano-effects.html

61 https://www.nationalgeographic.com/news/2018/02/neanderthals-cave-art-humans-evolution-science/

62 https://www.theguardian.com/science/2019/nov/27/bad-luck-may-have-caused-neanderthals-extinction-study

63 https://www.discovermagazine.com/planet-earth/how-much-neanderthal-dna-do-humans-have

64 https://www.livescience.com/60431-do-animals-murder-each-other.html

65 http://dx.doi.org/10.1038/nature16477

66 Watson P. Ideas: A History of Thought and Invention from Fire to Freud. 2005

67 https://www.smh.com.au/opinion/world-war-iv-will-be-fought-with-sticks-and-stones-20170421-gvpafh.html

68 https://stevenberlinjohnson.com

69 Graham Hancock has proposed an extensive case that ideas like agriculture uncovered at Gopekli Tepi may have been passed down from an earlier lost civilisation.

70 https://www.ancient.eu/uruk/

71 https://www.ancient.eu/article/846/cylinder-seals-in-ancient-mesopotamia---their-hist/

72 The Bishop's Brothel. By E.J Burford 1993

73 https://www.weforum.org/agenda/2018/10/how-the-agricultural-revolution-made-us-inequal

74 The Historical Encyclopaedia of World Slavery, Volume 1-7 By Junius P. Rodriguez

75 https://www.smithsonianmag.com/smart-news/midwests-new-slave-making-ant-species-uses-stealth-not-force-take-prisoners-180949318/

76 Ronald Segal, The Black Diaspora: Five Centuries of the Black Experience Outside Africa. 1995.

77 https://time.com/5171819/christianity-slavery-book-excerpt/

78 https://roaringwriters.org/quote/whenever-i-hear-anyone-arguing-for-slavery-i-feel-a-strong-impulse-to-see-it-tried-on-him-personally-abraham-lincoln-1809%C2%961865-address-to-an-indiana-regiment-march-17-1865/

79 https://www.washingtonpost.com/lifestyle/kidspost/abraham-lincoln-was-assassinated-150-years-ago/2015/04/07/9ebbacde-ce5b-11e4-8a46-b1dc9be5a8ff_story.html

80 https://www.globalslaveryindex.org
81 https://www.theguardian.com/news/2019/feb/25/modern-slavery-trafficking-persons-one-in-200
82 https://www.ancient.eu/uruk/
83 https://www.smithsonianmag.com/history/gobekli-tepe-the-worlds-first-temple-83613665/
84 https://nextcity.org/daily/entry/there-are-10000-cities-on-planet-earth-half-didnt-exist-40-years-ago
85 https://www.researchgate.net/publication/222521682_Urban_Density_and_Rate_of_Inventions
86 https://www.uspto.gov/web/offices/ac/ido/oeip/taf/h_counts.htm
87 https://www.britannica.com/topic/patent
88 https://www.uspto.gov/web/offices/ac/ido/oeip/taf/h_counts.htm
89 https://www.wipo.int/edocs/pubdocs/en/wipo_pub_941_2020.pdf
90 https://worldpopulationreview.com/world-cities
91 https://worldhappiness.report/ed/2020/urban-rural-happiness-differentials-across-the-world/
92 https://www.citylab.com/life/2017/08/the-geography-of-innovation/530349/
93 https://www.citylab.com/life/2017/08/the-geography-of-innovation/530349/
94 https://worldhappiness.report/ed/2020/urban-rural-happiness-differentials-across-the-world/
95 The Paradox Of Choice. Barry Schwartz © 2004
96 https://www.theguardian.com/lifeandstyle/wordofmouth/2013/may/08/restaurant-menu-psychology-tricks-order-more
97 https://www.britannica.com/technology/Moores-law
98 https://www.britannica.com/biography/Darius-I
99 https://www.historyofinformation.com/detail.php?id=131
100 Mehrdad Kia. The Persian Empire: A Historical Encyclopaedia . 2016
101 https://www.britannica.com/topic/Great-Wall-of-China
102 http://cultureandcommunication.org/deadmedia/index.php/Homing_Pigeons
103 https://www.pigeoncontrolresourcecentre.org/html/about-pigeons.html
104 https://www.history.com/topics/sports/olympic-games
105 https://vassallohistory.wordpress.com/carrier-pigeons/
106 https://medium.com/@interestingshit/carrier-pigeons-mother-natures-express-delivery-service-6226b4d837b6
107 https://www.thevintagenews.com/2017/03/04/the-mongol-empire-was-the-cradle-of-many-inventions-including-dried-milk-hand-grenades/
108 https://www.nam.ac.uk/explore/british-army-entrusted-its-secrets-birdbrains
109 https://www.si.edu/object/nmah_425415
110 https://www.telegraph.co.uk/news/2016/05/05/islamic-state-using-homing-pigeons-to-deliver-messages-to-operat/
111 https://www.metmuseum.org/toah/hd/book/hd_book.htm

112 https://www.history.com/topics/inventions/printing-press
113 Standage, Tom, *The Victorian Internet*, London: Weidenfeld & Nicolson 1998.
114 Gleick, J, The Information: a History, a Theory, a Flood, London, Fourth Estate, 2011
115 http://distantwriting.co.uk/companiesandforeigntraffic.html
116 https://atlantic-cable.com/Souvenirs/1866Medal/index.htm
117 http://www.yaleslavery.org/WhoYaleHonors/morse.html
118 http://www.seas.columbia.edu/marconi/history.html
119 https://www.history.com/this-day-in-history/marconi-sends-first-atlantic-wire-less-transmission
120 https://www.weforum.org/agenda/2019/04/how-much-data-is-generated-each-day-cf4bddf29f/
121 https://www.statista.com/statistics/617136/digital-population-worldwide/
122 https://www.statista.com/statistics/617136/digital-population-worldwide/
123 https://www.brandwatch.com/blog/twitter-stats-and-statistics/
124 https://wearesocial.com/blog/2020/01/digital-2020-3-8-billion-people-use-so-cial-media
125 https://syncedreview.com/2020/05/20/neural-network-ai-is-the-future-of-the-translation-industry/
126 https://www.cnbc.com/2018/10/02/steve-jobs-heres-what-most-people-get-wrong-about-focus.html
127 https://www.statista.com/topics/3928/reading-habits-in-the-us/
128 https://www.businessofapps.com/data/netflix-statistics/
129 Lieberman D. The Molecule of More. 2019.
130 https://www.drugabuse.gov/publications/research-reports/cocaine/how-does-cocaine-produce-its-effects
131 https://www.sciencemag.org/news/2018/01/dopamine-may-have-given-hu-mans-our-social-edge-over-other-apes
132 http://sitn.hms.harvard.edu/flash/2018/dopamine-smartphones-battle-time/
133 https://www.theguardian.com/technology/2018/mar/04/has-dopamine-got-us-hooked-on-tech-facebook-apps-addiction
134 A Theory of Human Motivation. A. H. Maslow. 1943.
135 https://kinsta.com/blog/facebook-statistics/
136 https://howmuch.net/articles/top-50-most-profitable-companies-in-the-us-2020
137 https://now.northropgrumman.com/this-is-your-brain-on-instagram-effects-of-social-media-on-the-brain/
138 https://www.google.com/about/philosophy.html
139 https://www.cnbc.com/2019/04/02/how-facebook-insta-gram-whatsapp-and-messenger-make-money.html
140 https://www.investopedia.com/ask/answers/120114/how-does-twitter-twtr-make-money.asp

141 https://now.northropgrumman.com/this-is-your-brain-on-instagram-effects-of-social-media-on-the-brain/

142 https://www.businessinsider.com/twitter-jack-dorsey-social-media-can-be-addictive-2020-11

143 https://about.fb.com/news/2019/10/mark-zuckerberg-stands-for-voice-and-free-expression/

144 https://www.theguardian.com/technology/2020/may/28/zuckerberg-facebook-police-online-speech-trump

145 https://parler.com/auth/access

146 https://www.businessinsider.com/parler-website-is-back-online-2021-1

147 https://founders.archives.gov/documents/Jefferson/01-09-02-0209

148 https://www.humanetech.com

149 https://www.wxyz.com/news/upfront/7-upfront-at-7pm-discussing-the-dangers-of-misinformation-with-tristan-harris-co-founder-of-the-center-for-humane-technology

150 https://www.seattletimes.com/nation-world/nation-politics/obama-makes-his-mark-as-first-social-media-president/

151 https://www.reuters.com/article/us-libya-gaddafi-finalhours-idUS-TRE79K43S20111021

152 https://cpj.org/2015/10/in-china-harsh-penalties-for-false-news-make-it-ha/

153 https://www.amnestyusa.org/reports/viet-nam-tech-giants-complicit-in-industrial-scale-repression/

154 https://thediplomat.com/2020/03/chinas-ubiquitous-facial-recognition-tech-sparks-privacy-backlash/

155 https://www.usnews.com/news/cities/articles/2020-08-14/the-top-10-most-surveilled-cities-in-the-world

156 https://www.nbcnews.com/tech/tech-news/foreign-governments-are-fed-social-media-threatening-prison-tech-employees-n993841

157 https://www.wired.com/story/inside-the-nsas-secret-tool-for-mapping-your-social-network/

158 https://cyber.fsi.stanford.edu/io/people/renee-diresta

159 https://www.intelligence.senate.gov/sites/default/files/documents/os-rdiresta-080118.pdf

160 https://www.intelligence.senate.gov/sites/default/files/documents/Report_Volume2.pdf

161 https://www.intelligence.senate.gov/sites/default/files/documents/Report_Volume2.pdf

162 https://www.intelligence.senate.gov/sites/default/files/documents/Report_Volume2.pdf

163 http://www.abrahamlincolnonline.org/lincoln/speeches/house.htm

164 https://biblia.com/bible/esv/matthew/12/22-32

165 https://qz.com/1498526/ex-russian-spies-say-social-media-is-why-the-us-is-losing/

166 https://humanetech.com
167 https://www.humanetech.com
168 http://humanetech.com/wp-content/uploads/2019/06/Testimony-Background-Tristan-Harris_CHT.pdf
169 https://www.washingtonpost.com/opinions/2020/04/27/chinese-propaganda-covid-19-grows-us-social-media-must-act/
170 https://www.nationsonline.org/oneworld/countries_of_the_world.htm
171 https://moneywise.com/a/americans-say-these-are-the-most-dishonest-professions
172 https://www.oxfordreference.com/view/10.1093/acref/9780191826719.001.0001/q-oro-ed4-00010168
173 https://www.ancient.eu/Pythia/
174 https://www.biblicalarchaeology.org/daily/ancient-cultures/daily-life-and-practice/the-oracle-of-delphi-was-she-really-stoned/
175 https://www.history.com/topics/ancient-greece/delphi
176 https://www.carlogos.org/reviews/largest-tire-manufacturers.html
177 https://www.newstatesman.com/blogs/the-faith-column/2007/03/ancient-greek-gods-greece
178 www.politico.com/story/2018/07/30/in-god-we-trust-becomes-nations-motto-july-30-1956-741016
179 https://www.history.com/this-day-in-history/president-eisenhower-signs-in-god-we-trust-into-law
180 https://www.gilderlehrman.org/history-resources/spotlight-primary-source/"defence-fort-mchenry"-or-"-star-spangled-banner"-1814
181 https://www.masjidtucson.org/God/trust_God_verses.html
182 https://news.gallup.com/poll/200186/five-key-findings-religion.aspx
183 Hepatology Principles and Practice. Erwin Kuntz. © 2001.
184 https://biblehub.com/ezekiel/21-21.htm
185 https://www.predictionx.org/haruspicy
186 https://www.encyclopedia.com/science/encyclopedias-almanacs-transcripts-and-maps/anthropomancy
187 http://www.actforlibraries.org/the-history-and-practice-of-anthropomancy/
188 https://listverse.com/2016/12/05/10-weird-fortune-telling-methods-from-history/
189 https://www.squarefoot.com.hk/en/lifestyle/the-traditions-of-kau-cim-35877/
190 https://matcha-jp.com/en/892
191 https://theculturetrip.com/south-america/bolivia/articles/yatiris-bolivian-fortune-tellers/
192 https://www.smithsonianmag.com/history/how-are-horoscopes-still-thing-180957701/
193 https://www.dandelionchandelier.com/2020/02/07/most-influencial-astrologers/

194 https://www.livescience.com/17943-oldest-astrologer-board-zodiac.html
195 https://www.theguardian.com/global/2018/mar/11/star-gazing-why-millennials-are-turning-to-astrology
196 https://www.sciencedaily.com/releases/2013/12/131210113409.htm
197 https://www.buzzfeed.com/sydrobinson1/2020-presidential-election-astrology
198 https://www.npr.org/sections/codeswitch/2013/08/26/215761377/a-history-of-snake-oil-salesmen
199 https://www.npr.org/sections/codeswitch/2013/08/26/215761377/a-history-of-snake-oil-salesmen
200 Gilman et al. Hysteria Beyond Freud. 1993
201 Hysteria Beyond Freud . Gilman et al. 1993
202 https://bjui-journals.onlinelibrary.wiley.com/doi/full/10.1046/j.1464-410X.2002.02911.x
203 Charlatan. America's Most Dangerous Huckster. Pope Brook. 2009
204 http://www.poachingfacts.com/faces-of-the-poachers/buyers-of-tiger-and-leopard-parts/
205 https://time.com/5835244/accidental-poisonings-trump/
206 https://www.cnbc.com/2020/05/18/trump-says-he-takes-hydroxychloroquine-to-prevent-coronavirus-infection.html
207 https://www.fda.gov/drugs/drug-safety-and-availability/fda-cautions-against-use-hydroxychloroquine-or-chloroquine-covid-19-outside-hospital-setting-or
208 https://edition.cnn.com/2020/05/22/health/hydroxychloroquine-sales-covid-19-trump-invs/index.html
209 https://www.aljazeera.com/news/2020/04/iran-700-dead-drinking-alcohol-cure-coronavirus-200427163529629.html
210 https://www.cnn.com/2020/03/30/europe/soviet-strongmen-coronavirus-intl/index.html
211 https://www.thespiritsbusiness.com/2014/01/worlds-largest-vodka-markets/2/
212 https://scroll.in/latest/954992/coronavirus-assam-bjp-mla-claims-cow-urine-dung-can-cure-the-illness
213 https://www.thehindu.com/news/national/coronavirus-group-hosts-cow-urine-party-says-covid-19-due-to-meat-eaters/article31070516.ece
214 https://www.ncbi.nlm.nih.gov/pmc/articles/PMC4566776/
215 https://www.theguardian.com/world/2020/mar/26/mexican-governor-miguel-barbosa-prompts-outrage-with-claim-poor-are-immune-to-covid-19
216 https://www.channelnewsasia.com/news/world/coronavirus-australia-nsw-man-tasered-toilet-roll-fight-tamworth-12504924
217 https://hbr.org/2011/08/henry-ford-never-said-the-fast
218 Sowden, M. Life changing inventions the experts said would never work. 2008.
219 http://www.thebasinandrange.com/story-behind-americas-first-road-trip/
220 https://www.cnbc.com/2020/01/06/us-auto-sales-down-in-2019-but-still-top-17-million.html

221 http://www.historygrandrapids.org/article/2290/the-detroit-episode-and-henry-

222 https://hbr.org/2011/08/henry-ford-never-said-the-fast

223 https://gizmodo.com/about-40-of-american-made-cars-in-1900-were-steam-powe-1597522738

224 https://gizmodo.com/about-40-of-american-made-cars-in-1900-were-steam-powe-1597522738

225 https://www.rsc.org/images/Arrhenius1896_tcm18-173546.pdf

226 https://www.rsc.org/images/Arrhenius1896_tcm18-173546.pdf

227 https://www.eei.org/issuesandpolicy/electrictransportation/Documents/FI-NAL_EV_Sales_Update_April2019.pdf

228 https://www.entrepreneur.com/article/295312

229 https://www.businessinsider.com/richard-branson-fails-virgin-companies-that-went-bust-2016-5

230 Branson. Like A Virgin. Secrets they won't teach you in business school © 2012

231 https://hbr.org/2013/01/five-of-steve-jobss-biggest-mi

232 https://news.stanford.edu/2005/06/14/jobs-061505/

233 https://genius.com/Steve-jobs-ipod-introduction-annotated

234 https://www.theatlantic.com/technology/archive/2013/10/12-years-ago-apples-ipod-spurs-mixed-reactions/280795/

235 https://qz.com/818085/apples-aapl-most-revolutionary-product-the-ipod-was-predicted-to-fail-15-years-ago/

236 Source: Yahoo Finance

237 https://qz.com/263306/a-memorial-for-the-classic-ipod-which-changed-apples-fortunes-forever/

238 https://www.apple.com/newsroom/2007/01/09Apple-Rein-vents-the-Phone-with-iPhone/

239 http://www.hp.com/hpinfo/abouthp/histnfacts/museum/personalsystems/0031/

240 Source: Yahoo Finance

241 https://www.bloomberg.com/news/articles/2016-11-04/steve-ballmer-says-smartphones-broke-his-relationship-with-bill-gates

242 https://kommandotech.com/statistics/how-many-iphones-have-been-sold-worldwide/

243 https://www.statista.com/statistics/263438/market-share-held-by-nokia-smart-phones-since-2007/

244 https://www.zdnet.com/article/nokia-where-it-all-went-wrong-by-the-man-who-made-it-the-worlds-biggest-mobile-company/

245 https://review42.com/what-percentage-of-startups-fail/

246 https://www.techwyse.com/blog/infographics/facebook-acquisitions-the-com-plete-list-infographic/

247 https://www.hrzone.com/lead/culture/why-did-google-abandon-20-time-for-innovation

248 https://qz.com/115831/googles-20-time-which-brought-you-gmail-and-ad-sense-is-now-as-good-as-dead/

249 https://en.wikipedia.org/wiki/List_of_mergers_and_acquisitions_by_Alphabet
250 https://asia.nikkei.com/Business/Masayoshi-Son-s-300-year-plan
251 https://www.cnbc.com/2020/08/11/softbank-2020-results.html
252 https://www.japantimes.co.jp/news/2020/06/25/business/corporate-business/softbank-masayoshi-son-alibaba-jack-ma/#.XzdzqC-w2jQ
253 https://www.japantimes.co.jp/news/2020/06/25/business/corporate-business/softbank-masayoshi-son-alibaba-jack-ma/#.XzdzqC-w2jQ
254 https://www.cnbc.com/2020/08/11/softbank-2020-results.html
255 https://www.forbes.com/sites/alexkonrad/2020/04/05/exclusive-interview-masayoshi-son-talks-wework-vision-fund-softbank/#666aecd47f41
256 https://www.forbes.com/sites/alexkonrad/2020/04/05/exclusive-interview-masayoshi-son-talks-wework-vision-fund-softbank/?sh=5ef916f87f41
257 https://www.businessinsider.com/wework-ipo-we-company-history-founder-story-timeline-adam-neumann-2019-8#something-clicked-for-neumann-and-mckelvey-they-saw-that-it-was-the-focus-on-community-not-sustainability-that-drove-people-to-green-desk-in-2010-they-sold-their-stake-and-began-we-work-5
258 https://news.crunchbase.com/news/wework-may-reduce-its-valuation-ahead-of-ipo-by-tens-of-billions/
259 https://www.wsj.com/articles/softbank-mulls-investment-of-over-1-billion-in-wework-1485814702
260 https://www.thenational.ae/business/economy/wework-wins-4-4bn-from-two-investment-groups-1.622739
261 https://asia.nikkei.com/Spotlight/Sharing-Economy/SoftBank-s-Son-says-We-Work-is-his-next-Alibaba
262 https://time.com/collection/genius-companies-2018/5412659/wework/
263 https://www.bloomberg.com/news/articles/2020-04-02/adam-neumann-ousted-from-billionaire-ranks-on-softbank-reversal?sref=BWbpWjRm
264 https://www.fastcompany.com/90325201/wework-reported-nearly-2-billion-in-losses-in-2018
265 https://www.theatlantic.com/technology/archive/2019/09/why-wework-was-destined-fail/598891/
266 https://www.theguardian.com/business/2019/sep/30/wework-scraps-share-sale-adam-neumann
267 https://www.vanityfair.com/news/2019/09/adam-neumann-wework-resigned
268 https://www.cnbc.com/2020/08/11/softbank-2020-results.html
269 https://www.forbes.com/sites/alexkonrad/2020/04/05/exclusive-interview-masayoshi-son-talks-wework-vision-fund-softbank/#5212b13c7f41
270 https://www.buzzfeednews.com/article/nitashatiku/how-wework-convinced-investors-its-worth-billions
271 https://www.buzzfeednews.com/article/nitashatiku/how-wework-convinced-investors-its-worth-billions

272 https://www.buzzfeednews.com/article/nitashatiku/how-wework-convinced-investors-its-worth-billions

273 https://www.wsj.com/articles/wework-a-20-billion-startup-fueled-by-silicon-valley-pixie-dust-1508424483

274 https://www.bloomberg.com/news/articles/2020-04-02/adam-neumann-ousted-from-billionaire-ranks-on-softbank-reversal

275 https://www.straitstimes.com/business/companies-markets/wework-softbank-fail-to-get-suit-over-stock-deal-dismissed

276 https://www.ft.com/content/62956815-36db-4608-af74-763a023907ea

277 https://www.washingtonpost.com/wp-srv/national/daily/nov98/nazicars30.htm

278 https://rarehistoricalphotos.com/henry-ford-grand-cross-1938/

279 https://www.thehenryford.org/collections-and-research/digital-collections/sets/10948

280 The People's Tycoon: Henry Ford and the American Century. Stephen Watts 2006

281 https://www.lovemoney.com/gallerylist/74533/richest-person-every-decade-1820-2020

282 https://www.sciencedaily.com/releases/2009/07/090701082720.htm

283 Zajonc, Robert B. (1968). "Attitudinal Effects Of Mere Exposure" Journal of Personality and Social Psychology.

284 https://www.statista.com/statistics/271258/facebooks-advertising-revenue-worldwide/

285 https://www.emarketer.com/newsroom/index.php/us-political-ad-spending-to-hit-record-high/

286 https://www.vieodesign.com/blog/new-data-why-people-hate-ads

287 https://www.sciencedirect.com/science/article/abs/pii/002210319290055O

288 Encyclopaedia of Social Psychology. Edited by Baumeister and Vohs. © 2007

289 http://psychology.iresearchnet.com/social-psychology/social-influence/mere-exposure-effect/

290 https://www.neuroscience.org.uk/proximity-mere-exposure-effect-social-psychology/

291 https://www.imdb.com/title/tt1068699/episodes?season=1&ref_=tt_eps_sn_1

292 https://premier-research.com/blog/perpectives-placebo-problem-part-14-brief-history-placebo/

293 https://www.knowablemagazine.org/article/mind/2017/imagination-effect-history-placebo-power

294 https://www.ncbi.nlm.nih.gov/pmc/articles/PMC2601307/

295 https://www.knowablemagazine.org/article/mind/2017/imagination-effect-history-placebo-power

296 https://premier-research.com/blog/perpectives-placebo-problem-part-14-brief-history-placebo/

297 https://www.nhs.uk/news/medical-practice/survey-finds-97-of-gps-prescribe-placebos/

298 PBS Digital Studios. How The Placebo Effect Tricks Your Brain. © 2015.

299 https://www.health.harvard.edu/blog/placebo-can-work-even-know-placebo-201607079926

300 https://www.medpagetoday.com/tedmed/tedmed/83377

301 https://pubmed.ncbi.nlm.nih.gov/10812563/

302 https://www.advisory.com/daily-briefing/2017/08/03/sham-surgery

303 https://journals.plos.org/plosbiology/article?id=10.1371/journal.pbio.1002570

304 https://flavourjournal.biomedcentral.com/articles/10.1186/2044-7248-2-29

305 https://www.npr.org/blogs/thesalt/2013/06/30/196708393/from-farm-to-fork-to-plate-how-utensils-season-your-meal

306 https://www.npr.org/blogs/thesalt/2013/06/30/196708393/from-farm-to-fork-to-plate-how-utensils-season-your-meal

307 https://www.studyfinds.org/placebo-effect-broken-heart/

308 https://www.bbc.com/future/article/20200501-the-performance-enhancing-trick-to-being-a-better-athlete

309 https://bleacherreport.com/articles/1520496-how-important-is-home-court-advantage-in-the-nba

310 https://www.gsb.stanford.edu/faculty-research/publications/placebo-effects-marketing-actions-consumer-may-get-what-they-pay

311 https://coolmarketingstuff.com/the-placebo-effect-and-marketing/

312 https://www.pbs.org/wgbh/frontline/article/colin-powell-u-n-speech-was-a-great-intelligence-failure/

313 https://www.jstor.org/stable/41940146

314 https://www.pbs.org/wgbh/frontline/article/colin-powell-u-n-speech-was-a-great-intelligence-failure/

315 https://poll.qu.edu/national/release-detail?ReleaseID=385

316 https://2001-2009.state.gov/secretary/former/powell/remarks/2003/17300.htm

317 ttps://2001-2009.state.gov/secretary/former/powell/remarks/2003/17300.htm

318 https://2001-2009.state.gov/secretary/former/powell/remarks/2003/17300.htm

319 https://news.gallup.com/poll/7720/powells-un-appearance-important-public.aspx

320 https://www.washingtonpost.com/wp-srv/politics/polls/vault/stories/data020603.htm

321 https://www.politico.com/story/2015/01/poll-republicans-wmds-iraq-114016

322 https://www.nti.org/gsn/article/powell-blames-himself-iraqi-wmd-speech-un/

323 https://www.washingtonpost.com/news/politics/wp/2018/03/20/15-years-after-it-began-the-death-toll-from-the-iraq-war-is-still-murky/

324 https://www.nytimes.com/2006/06/08/world/middleeast/08cnd-iraq.html?_r=0

325 https://en.wikipedia.org/wiki/Atiyah_Abd_al-Rahman

326 http://www.andyworthington.co.uk/2017/10/03/life-after-guantanamo-the-story-of-mourad-benchellali-freed-13-years-ago-but-still-stigmatized/

327 https://northafricapost.com/14213-france-wanted-ex-gia-islamist-nabbed-switzerland.html

[328] https://www.businessinsider.com/us-taxpayers-spent-8000-each-2-trillion-iraq-war-study-2020-2

[329] https://www.wealthypersons.com/dick-cheney-net-worth-2020-2021/

[330] https://theweek.com/articles/472697/kofi-annans-memoir-did-colin-powell-doubt-wmd-claims

[331] https://www.celebritynetworth.com/richest-politicians/presidents/tony-blair-net-worth/

[332] https://www.lovemoney.com/gallerylist/64364/people-making-a-fortune-from-public-speaking

[333] https://www.nih.gov/news-events/news-releases/nih-human-microbiome-project-defines-normal-bacterial-makeup-body

[334] https://depts.washington.edu/ceeh/downloads/FF_Microbiome.pdf

[335] https://www.nih.gov/news-events/news-releases/nih-human-microbiome-project-defines-normal-bacterial-makeup-body

[336] https://microbiomejournal.biomedcentral.com/articles/10.1186/s40168-019-0619-4

[337] https://www.amnh.org/exhibitions/the-secret-world-inside-you/microbiome-at-birth

[338] https://www.amnh.org/exhibitions/the-secret-world-inside-you/microbiome-at-birth

[339] https://www.ncbi.nlm.nih.gov/pmc/articles/PMC7019891/

[340] https://www.pnas.org/content/105/48/18964

[341] http://www.mostlymicrobes.com/breast-milk-sugars/

[342] https://www.statnews.com/2017/06/09/microbiome-human-evolution/

[343] https://www.ncbi.nlm.nih.gov/pmc/articles/PMC4367209/

[344] https://www.ncbi.nlm.nih.gov/pmc/articles/PMC4367209/

[345] https://www.nature.com/articles/d41586-020-00198-y

[346] https://www.nature.com/articles/d41586-020-00198-y

[347] https://www.reuters.com/article/us-health-csection-brain/possible-link-between-c-section-and-autism-adhd-idUSKCN1VI1VS

[348] https://www.joinsprouttherapy.com/autism/effects-of-breastfeeding

[349] https://asunow.asu.edu/20190409-discoveries-autism-symptoms-reduced-nearly-50-percent-two-years-after-fecal-transplant

[350] https://scholar.harvard.edu/files/jenniferlerner/files/annual_review_manuscript_june_16_final.final_.pdf

[351] https://scholar.harvard.edu/files/jenniferlerner/files/annual_review_manuscript_june_16_final.final_.pdf

[352] On Anger: De Ira by Seneca © 2017

[353] https://www.ncbi.nlm.nih.gov/pmc/articles/PMC6287679/#CIT0007

[354] https://www.ncbi.nlm.nih.gov/pmc/articles/PMC6287679/#CIT0007

[355] P. Bercik, et al. The intestinal microbiota affect central levels of brain-derived neurotropic factor and behaviour in mice Gastroenterology, 141. 2011.

356 https://www.sciencedirect.com/science/article/pii/S2452231719300181#b0080
357 https://www.sciencedirect.com/science/article/pii/S2452231719300181#b0080
358 https://ourworldindata.org/mental-health
359 https://www.ncbi.nlm.nih.gov/pmc/articles/PMC6511407/
360 https://www.nature.com/articles/d42859-019-00019-x
361 https://www.economist.com/graphic-detail/2018/04/02/antibiotic-use-is-rapid-ly-increasing-in-developing-countries
362 https://www.pewtrusts.org/en/research-and-analysis/issue-briefs/2018/08/trends-in-us-antibiotic-use-2018
363 https://www.statnews.com/2017/06/09/microbiome-human-evolution/
364 https://genomebiology.biomedcentral.com/articles/10.1186/s13059-019-1807-z
365 https://genomebiology.biomedcentral.com/articles/10.1186/s13059-019-1807-z
366 https://www.science.org.au/curious/people-medicine/ancient-microbiome
367 https://ourworldindata.org/how-urban-is-the-world
368 https://www.npr.org/sections/goatsandsoda/2018/10/12/656198429/rate-of-c-sections-is-rising-at-an-alarming-rate
369 https://pubmed.ncbi.nlm.nih.gov/26267407/
370 https://pubmed.ncbi.nlm.nih.gov/27793228/
371 https://www.history.com/news/9-things-you-may-not-know-about-the-ancient-sumerians
372 Bernard Lietaer. The Future of Money. 1997.
373 https://www.storyofmathematics.com/sumerian.html
374 https://www.storyofmathematics.com/sumerian.html
375 https://www.bbc.co.uk/programmes/articles/1XkbKQwt49MpxWpsJ2zp-fQk/13-mammoth-facts-about-mammoths
376 https://asmedigitalcollection.asme.org/memagazineselect/article/140/09/31/366620/Celestial-GearboxThe-Oldest-Known-Computer-is-a
377 https://www.nature.com/news/archimedes-legendary-sphere-brought-to-life-1.18431
378 https://www.scientificamerican.com/article/a-chronicle-of-timekeeping-2006-02/
379 https://www.census.gov/history/www/innovations/technology/tabulation_and_processing.html
380 https://www.census.gov/history/www/census_then_now/notable_alumni/herman_hollerith.html
381 https://www.ibm.com/ibm/history/exhibits/logo/logo_4.html
382 https://www.ibm.com/ibm/history/ibm100/us/en/icons/founded/
383 https://www.statista.com/topics/1325/ibm/
384 http://www.rutherfordjournal.org/article040101.html
385 Edwin Black. IBM and The Holocaust © 2001
386 Edwin Black. IBM and The Holocaust © 2001
387 https://technical.ly/philly/2011/02/15/eniac-10-things-you-should-know-about-the-original-modern-super-computer-65-years-later/

[388] https://www.digitaltrends.com/computing/remembering-eniac-and-the-women-who-programmed-it/
[389] https://money.cnn.com/interactive/technology/computing-power-timeline/
[390] https://www.britannica.com/technology/ENIAC
[391] https://www.atomicheritage.org/history/computing-and-manhattan-project
[392] https://www.historyofinformation.com/detail.php?id=639
[393] MacRae, Norman. John Von Neumann: The Scientific Genius Who Pioneered the Modern Computer, Game Theory, Nuclear Deterrence, and Much More. 1992
[394] MacRae, Norman. John Von Neumann: The Scientific Genius Who Pioneered the Modern Computer, Game Theory, Nuclear Deterrence, and Much More. 1992
[395] https://www.bbc.com/news/world-asia-33755182
[396] Norman Macrae John Von Neumann: The Scientific Genius Who Pioneered the Modern Computer, Game Theory, Nuclear Deterrence, and Much More. © 1992
[397] https://www.historyofinformation.com/detail.php?id=639
[398] https://lemelson.mit.edu/resources/john-mauchly-j-presper-eckert
[399] https://www.unisys.com/aboutus/company-history
[400] https://www.app5.unisys.com/investors/annuals/2019_UnisysAnnualReport.pdf
[401] https://www.statista.com/statistics/203734/global-smartphone-penetration-per-capita-since-2005/
[402] https://www.intel.com/content/www/us/en/silicon-innovations/moores-law-technology.html
[403] https://www.statista.com/statistics/617136/digital-population-worldwide/
[404] https://www.nasdaq.com/glossary/h/high-frequency-trading
[405] https://www.cnbc.com/2018/08/03/how-do-airlines-price-seat-tickets.html
[406] https://bdtechtalks.com/2020/04/09/what-is-narrow-artificial-intelligence-ani/
[407] https://www.brookings.edu/blog/usc-brookings-schaeffer-on-health-policy/2019/03/05/will-robots-replace-doctors/
[408] https://www.technewsworld.com/story/86521.html
[409] https://www.forbes.com/sites/cognitiveworld/2019/07/05/how-ai-is-transforming-agriculture/#65ab02a64ad1
[410] https://www.who.int/news-room/fact-sheets/detail/road-traffic-injuries
[411] https://www.cnbc.com/2020/01/02/deaths-from-commercial-airplane-crashes-fell-more-than-50percent-in-2019.html
[412] https://www.frontiersin.org/articles/10.3389/fpsyg.2019.02415/full
[413] https://futurism.com/the-byte/tesla-autopilot-safer-average-driver
[414] https://electrek.co/2020/07/23/tesla-self-driving-elon-musk-house-to-work/
[415] https://www.nature.com/articles/d41586-018-07135-0
[416] https://www.moralmachine.net
[417] https://www.nature.com/articles/d41586-018-07135-0
[418] https://www.zdnet.com/article/how-autonomous-vehicles-could-save-over-350k-lives-in-the-us-and-millions-worldwide/

419 https://neuralink.com/about/
420 https://www.bloomberg.com/news/articles/2021-02-01/elon-musk-wired-up-a-monkey-s-brain-to-play-videogames
421 https://techcrunch.com/2020/08/28/take-a-closer-look-at-elon-musks-neuralink-surgical-robot/
422 https://neuralink.com/applications/
423 https://www.theverge.com/2019/9/23/20881032/facebook-ctrl-labs-acquisition-neural-interface-armband-ar-vr-deal
424 https://www.cnbc.com/2019/10/10/zuckerberg-says-brain-reading-wearables-come-before-implantables.html
425 https://www.nature.com/articles/s41593-020-0608-8
426 https://research.fb.com/category/augmented-reality-virtual-reality/
427 https://www.smalltechnews.com/archives/65047
428 https://www.zju.edu.cn/english/2020/0331/c19573a2019025/page.htm
429 https://www.meltin.jp/en/
430 https://www.hisour.com/cyborg-43050/
431 https://www.alliedmarketresearch.com/brain-computer-interfaces-market
432 https://www.vox.com/recode/2020/8/28/21404802/elon-musk-neuralink-brain-machine-interface-research
433 https://www.livescience.com/58790-crispr-explained.html
434 https://www.iflscience.com/plants-and-animals/forget-about-designer-babies-gene-editing-won-t-work-complex-traits-intelligence/
435 https://www.cnbc.com/2018/03/13/elon-musk-at-sxsw-a-i-is-more-dangerous-than-nuclear-weapons.html
436 https://arxiv.org/abs/1705.08807
437 https://www.reuters.com/article/uber-selfdriving/safety-driver-in-fatal-arizona-uber-self-driving-car-crash-charged-with-homicide-idUSKBN26708P
438 https://techcrunch.com/2020/03/02/waymo-brings-in-2-25-billion-from-outside-investors-alphabet/
439 https://waymo.com
440 https://www.worldhunger.org/world-child-hunger-facts/
441 https://www.un.org/development/desa/disabilities/envision2030-goal2.html
442 https://globalnutritionreport.org/reports/2020-global-nutrition-report/inequalities-global-burden-malnutrition/
443 https://globalnutritionreport.org/reports/2020-global-nutrition-report/inequalities-global-burden-malnutrition/
444 https://www.usda.gov/foodwaste/faqs
445 https://www.worldvision.org/hunger-news-stories/food-waste
446 https://www.worldvision.org/hunger-news-stories/food-waste
447 https://www.epa.gov/sustainable-management-food/reduce-wasted-food-feeding-animals
448 https://abcnews.go.com/US/wireStory/donations-pigs-part-las-vegas-efforts-cut-food-62687046

449 Edwin Black. IBM and The Holocaust © 2001

450 https://www.britannica.com/technology/ENIAC

451 https://www.wired.com/2012/06/june-27-1954-worlds-first-nuclear-power-plant-opens/

452 https://www.eia.gov/energyexplained/nuclear/us-nuclear-industry.php

453 https://www.businessinsider.com/map-every-nuclear-bomb-explosion-history-2015-10

454 https://www.cnbc.com/2017/09/04/putin-leader-in-artificial-intelligence-will-rule-world.html

455 https://fas.org/sgp/crs/natsec/R45178.pdf

456 https://www.forbes.com/sites/davidaxe/2020/06/30/dont-panic-but-russia-is-training-its-robot-tanks-to-understand-human-speech/#5125d74114f2

457 https://thestrategybridge.org/the-bridge/2020/10/8/autonomous-systems-in-the-combat-environment-the-key-or-the-curse-to-the-us

458 https://fas.org/sgp/crs/natsec/R45178.pdf

459 https://www.army-technology.com/features/china-ai-arms-race/

460 https://www.nature.com/articles/d41586-019-02360-7

461 https://www.army-technology.com/features/china-ai-arms-race/

462 https://www.globaltimes.cn/content/1149168.shtml

463 https://www.albawaba.com/news/china-selling-autonomous-weaponized-drones-saudi-arabia-and-pakistan-1321951

464 https://www.army-technology.com/features/china-ai-arms-race/

465 https://breakingdefense.com/2019/09/dod-growth-in-artificial-intelligence-the-frontline-of-a-new-age-in-defense/

466 https://www.nationaldefensemagazine.org/articles/2020/2/3/analysts-say-$25-billion-needed-annually-for-ai

467 Schulman, Sander, and Christian, "The Rocky Relationship Between Washington and Silicon Valley: Clearing the Path to Improved Collaboration, 2017.

468 https://news.clearancejobs.com/2020/07/16/google-and-pentagon-relationship-post-project-maven/

469 https://thestrategybridge.org/the-bridge/2020/10/8/autonomous-systems-in-the-combat-environment-the-key-or-the-curse-to-the-us

470 https://news.un.org/en/story/2019/03/1035381

471 https://www.hrw.org/report/2020/08/10/stopping-killer-robots/country-positions-banning-fully-autonomous-weapons-and

472 https://medium.com/cantors-paradise/the-unparalleled-genius-of-john-von-neumann-791bb9f42a2d

473 https://www.history.com/topics/great-depression/great-depression-history

474 Paul A. Samuelson, William D. Nordhaus. Economics 19th Edition, International Edition 2009.

475 https://apps.bea.gov/scb/account_articles/general/0100od/maintext.htm

476 https://ourworldindata.org/grapher/world-population-in-extreme-poverty-absolute

477 https://www.oxfam.org/en/press-releases/worlds-billionaires-have-more-wealth-46-billion-people

478 https://www.moneycontrol.com/news/photos/world/in-charts-jeff-bezos-net-worth-how-big-is-it-check-out-comparison-5763311-4.html

479 https://www.pewsocialtrends.org/2020/01/09/trends-in-income-and-wealth-inequality/

480 https://www.newsweek.com/world-277-trillion-debt-so-why-arent-economists-more-worried-1549818

481 https://www.archives.gov/founding-docs/declaration-transcript

482 https://www.jfklibrary.org/learn/about-jfk/the-kennedy-family/robert-f-kennedy/robert-f-kennedy-speeches/remarks-at-the-university-of-kansas-march-18-1968

483 http://gnh.institute/gross-national-happiness-gnh-origin.htm

484 https://www.forbes.com/sites/jamesellsmoor/2019/07/11/new-zealand-ditches-gdp-for-happiness-and-wellbeing/?sh=2b9232e61942

485 https://www.independent.co.uk/travel/news-and-advice/finland-happiest-country-united-nations-world-happiness-report-a9414201.html

486 https://www.theguardian.com/sustainable-business/2014/sep/23/genuine-progress-indicator-gdp-gpi-vermont-maryland

487 https://science.time.com/2011/08/05/why-the-apes-arent-going-to-rise/

488 https://www.forbes.com/sites/victorlipman/2018/09/25/the-best-sentence-i-ever-read-about-managing-talent/?sh=712d5319cdfb

489 http://www.bbc.com/earth/story/20150929-why-are-we-the-only-human-species-still-alive

490 Kennedy R. Seattle World's Fair, August 7, 1962.

MATTHEW GODFREY has spent his entire career in the creation and management of ideas as a leader in the marketing and innovation industries. He is currently the CEO of a Food Technology company, Nutrition Innovation which been awarded Top 10 Start-up by FI Europe 2017, Best New Ingredient by the World Food Awards and the Asia Food Innovation Awards 2019, Global Agri-Food Tech Winner by Slingshot 2019, One of Singapore's Top 20 Start-ups 2019 and part of the Global FoodTech 500 in both 2019 and 2020.

In 2009, 2013, 2014, and 2015 he was a finalist for Campaign's APAC CEO of the Year, as well as Marketing Asia's Agency Professional of the Year and voted by the APAC Advertising Industry as one of Campaign's Most Admired Leaders in Asia Pacific. In 2015, he was named by Mumbrella as winner of The Asia Pacific CEO Of The Year for Advertising professionals.

Printed in Great Britain
by Amazon